Stanley G

Collect British Coins

James Mackay

1st edition 2004

Stanley Gibbons Ltd
London and Ringwood

Published by **Stanley Gibbons Ltd**
Editorial, Publications Sales Offices and Distribution Centre:
Parkside, Christchurch Road, Ringwood, Hants BH24 3SH

First Edition – March 2004

© Stanley Gibbons Ltd 2004

ISBN:0-85259-558-1

Item No. 2974 (04)

Printed in Great Britain by Pardy and Sons (Printers) Ltd

CONTENTS

INTRODUCTION

From the Gallo-Belgic gold staters of the 2nd century BC to the crown-sized commemorative pieces of the present day, the coins of Great Britain are highly popular with collectors. Collect British Coins presents a simplified catalogue of more than 2,000 years of British coinage, including Scotland, Ireland, the Isle of Man and the Channel Islands. It does not seek to provide detailed listings of every variety nor a full range of prices. Stanley Gibbons Limited do not deal in coins, but the prices quoted here represent an average for coins in reasonable condition. From 1950, however, prices are for coins in uncirculated condition. Remember that this is a rule of thumb and is intended merely as a rough guide to values. Many factors have to be taken into account in assessing the worth of any particular coin, and these are summarised in a separate section dealing with grades of condition.

Similarly, in a simplified catalogue of this nature it is impossible to itemise different dates, far less varieties and sub-types, mint-marks, privy marks and die variants, all of which may have an important bearing on the true value of a coin. For more detailed information the reader should consult the catalogues and monographs listed in the Select Bibliography.

Scope. Collect British Coins comprises:

- All coins according to major types (obverse and reverse)
- Year sets and proofs (where relevant)
- Coins of England to 1707 and Great Britain (or the United Kingdom) thereafter
- Coins of Scotland from David I (1124–53) to the Union in 1707
- Coins of Ireland from 995 to 1823
- Coins of the Isle of Man from 1709 to 1839 and 1965 to the present day
- Coins of Guernsey (since 1830) and Jersey (since 1841)

Size of illustrations. Coins are illustrated full size, unless otherwise specified.

Prices. Prices quoted in this catalogue are average prices for coins in good average condition, based on the prevailing market as exemplified in dealers' lists and auction realisations. It should be borne in mind that coins in better than average condition may be worth considerably more, while coins in worn or damaged condition will be heavily discounted.

Layout. Coins are set out chronologically according to reign or date of issue and in ascending order of denomination within each series.

SURVEY OF BRITISH COINS

The British Isles, being on the fringe of Europe and far removed from the great centres of Mediterranean civilisation, were relatively late in replacing barter with coined money. Half a millennium after the first coins were struck in Asia Minor in the mid-seventh century BC, crude copies of gold staters of Philip of Macedon (father of Alexander the Great) were being produced by the Celtic tribes and as they migrated westward, up the Danube and thence to Gaul (modern France) and Belgium, these coins became more and more blundered in the process, until latterly they bore hardly any resemblance to the Greek originals which had a laureated profile of Apollo on one side and a horse on the other. By the time the Belgic tribes crossed the Channel and settled in southern Britain, little more than a travesty of Apollo's hair and head-band or the merest outline of a horse remained.

These crude coins, utterly devoid of inscription, have a charm of their own. By the time the Romans were beginning to take an interest in Britain, the Apollo and horse motifs had developed into elaborate curvilinear motifs, found in both gold and silver coins. About 35 BC the Atrebates and Regni who occupied parts of the Home Counties, produced coins that bore abbreviated names of rulers, and this was soon imitated by other tribes, such as the Cantii (Kent) and the Catuvellauni north of the Thames. Among the native rulers who made their mark in history were Caratacus (Caradog), Cunobelin (the Cymbeline of Shakespeare's play) and Prasutagus of the Iceni, husband of the celebrated female warrior Boudicca (Boadicea).

Although Julius Caesar visited Britain in 54 BC it was not until AD 43 that the Romans invaded Britain. Within a few years they had conquered southern Britain, roughly equivalent to modern England, erected Hadrian's Wall and later the Antonine Wall (across the isthmus of the Forth and Clyde) to keep the Caledonians at bay. From the middle of the first century till the early fifth century, imperial coinage circulated in Roman Britain, but occasionally Roman coins had reverse motifs that alluded to their most westerly province and, indeed, the seated figures of Britannia on the coins of Antoninus Pius would later serve as the model for the first

copper halfpence and farthings in the reign of James II. In AD 287 Carausius, commander of the Roman Channel fleet, broke away and proclaimed a separate British Empire. Until his secessionist state was suppressed in 296 and Carausius was murdered, coins were struck at London.

In 407 the Roman legions were withdrawn from Britain for the defence of Rome itself. Roman Britain now entered the period known as the Dark Ages. Law and order soon broke down and the inhabitants reverted to barter as the money supply rapidly vanished. For almost two centuries anarchy reigned in the former Roman province, ravaged by constant attacks by Germanic tribes, the Angles, Saxons and Jutes who gradually carved out their own kingdoms. Peace and commerce were restored from the late sixth century onwards and this was reflected in the emergence of distinctive coinage in the various petty kingdoms. Their money was modelled on the coinage that developed in Europe; thus the gold thrymsa of Kent was based on the tremissis of the Merovingian Franks while the silver sceat of Northumbria derived its name from the Germanic word for 'treasure'.

About 755 Pepin, father of Charlemagne, began striking silver deniers, a revival of the Roman denarius. This served as the model for the silver penny pioneered soon afterwards by Offa, King of Mercia, and the ancestor of the coins which provided the bulk of the money in England for more than five centuries. The Frankish system of money, based on the libra (pound) of 20 solidi (shillings) divided into 12 denarii (pennies), remained in use in Britain until £sd was replaced by decimal currency in 1971. Silver pennies were struck not only by each of the kingdoms that preceded the unification of England under Alfred of Wessex in the late ninth century, but also by the Vikings in the Danelaw and even by the archbishops of Canterbury and York. In fact, ecclesiastical coinage, mainly confined to pennies, continued until Henry VIII broke with Rome in the 16th century.

Anglo-Saxon pennies had a crude effigy of the king on the obverse (heads) while the reverse (tails) generally gave the place of minting and even the name of the individual moneyer. About 120 towns and cities are known to have struck coins, the 'coining irons' (as the dies were known) being supplied from London to ensure a measure of uniformity.

This system continued under the Norman kings. Superficially the thin silver hammered pennies which survived till the time of Henry VII seem very similar, but apart from the inscriptions there is a great diversity of coin types. From the 11th century onwards a cross appeared on the reverse, partly for religious reasons but mainly as a guide to cutting coins into halves or quarters to create halfpence and farthings, although distinctive halfpennies were produced sporadically from the reign of Henry I onwards. The styles of the coins at various times are known by the type of cross used, such as Short Cross, Long Cross and Cross-Crosslet.

The Long Cross coinage was introduced in 1247, in the reign of Henry III, and is so-called because the cross extended all the way to the edge of the coin as a safeguard against clipping. In 1279 Edward I expanded the coinage to include halfpence and farthings on a regular basis, but also struck the groat, a large silver coin worth fourpence. This imitated the larger silver coins which were then beginning to circulate on the Continent and known as a gros (French for 'large'). The experiment was not successful and no groats were minted between 1282 and 1351 when Edward III revived this denomination. In this period the number of mints gradually decreased and by the 15th century these were identified merely by an initial letter, such as B (Bristol), C (Coventry) or E (York, from its Latin name Eboracum).

It was in 1334, during the reign of Edward III, that the system of marking coins with a symbol corresponding to the Trial of the Pyx was adopted. These marks, changed at intervals, enable numismatists to place subsequent issues in broadly chronological order.

Edward III was also the first English monarch to issue gold coins on a regular basis (a few gold pennies or dinars modelled on Arabic coins had been struck in Anglo-Saxon times). In 1344 Edward launched the double-leopard or florin worth 72 pence, along with the leopard (half-florin) and helm (quarter-florin) the coins taking their English names from their chief motifs, but consciously imitating the Continental gold coins pioneered by the Italian city of Florence. This scheme was a failure and

the coins were quickly replaced by heavier pieces. The noble (6s 8d or a third of a pound) showed the monarch armed and standing in a warship, allegedly a reference to the English naval victory over the French at Sluys in the first phase of the Hundred Years War. By the Treaty of Bretigny Edward relinquished his claim to the French throne and dropped the French title from his coins, but when war broke out again in 1369 the reference to France was restored – and would remain on English (and later British coins) right down to the defeat of Napoleon and the restoration of the Bourbon monarchy.

During the Wars of the Roses the value of precious metals, especially gold, fluctuated considerably and this necessitated some radical changes in the coins. The weight of the penny was reduced to 12 grains in 1464 and the value of the noble was raised to 8s 4d, an awkward sum. A year later it was replaced by the Rose Noble or Ryal of 120 grains, tariffed at 10 shillings. Because there continued a need for a coin worth a third of a pound (6s 8d) yet another coin was then introduced. Weighing 80 grains, this was the Angel, so-called on account of the figure of the Archangel Michael slaying the serpent (obverse). The reverse, however, retained the medieval galleon with the monarch amidships. Because of its religious significance, the Angel was highly prized as a talisman and was also used in the ceremony of touching for King's Evil (scrofula), which successive monarchs down to the end of the Stuart dynasty carried out faithfully. As an angel was suspended round the neck of the sufferer from a cord, the great majority of extant examples have been pierced at the top.

English coins continued in the medieval style, with stylised portraits that probably bore no resemblance to the living monarch, but the advent of the Tudor dynasty in 1485 saw a gradual change that brought the coinage into line with Continental counterparts. Under Henry VII the designs and lettering of the coins were modernised and new denominations were introduced, notably the gold sovereign (1489) and the silver testoon or shilling at the beginning of the 16th century, the first of the true portrait coins in England.

This established the pattern for the coinage throughout the Tudor period, although there were further innovations, notably the crown of five shillings (1551), not only the largest silver coin up to that time but also the first coin to bear a proper date in Arabic numerals. This practice gradually spread to other denominations although it did not become a general rule until the Commonwealth under Cromwell and mint-marks continued to be used until the late 17th century. Other changes in the Tudor era included the drastic debasement of the silver coins in the last years of Henry VIII, the countermarking of these base coins by Edward VI when they were reduced in face value, the remarkable 'face to face' coins of Mary Tudor showing her husband Philip II of Spain, and the introduction of the portcullis dollar in 1600, the first coin designed primarily for overseas trade

In the mid-16th century the use of 'fine' gold (almost 24 carat pure) was abandoned for every day usage although it continued to be used for certain denominations such as the ryal and angel into the Jacobean period. Instead a much more durable alloy known as 'crown' gold (because it was originally used for gold coins worth 5s) was adopted. This alloy, 22 carat (.917 fine) has been used for the great majority of British coins ever since. Until the reign of Elizabeth I all coins were struck by hand, skilled craftsmen wielding heavy hammers to produce them. Under French technicians, first Eloi Mestrell in the 1550s and later Nicolas Briot in the 1630s, the first experiments in milled coinage were conducted, although it was not until 1662 that milled coins became the general rule.

The most complex reign, from the numismatic viewpoint, was that of Charles I (1625–49). Although coin production was centralised by that time (at the Tower of London), a branch mint was established at Aberystwyth to coin silver from the Welsh mines. On the outbreak of the Civil War in 1642 Parliament gained control of the Tower Mint, while the Royalists moved the branch mint from Aberystwyth to Shrewsbury and later to Oxford where the college plate was soon melted down and converted into coins. While the Tower continued to strike coins in the name of the King, the Royalists produced some of the most fascinating coins of all time, including the giant triple unite (£3) silver coins with their panoramic view of Oxford on the obverse. Later, various Royalist strongholds besieged by the Roundheads struck their own makeshift coins, some of which continued to be produced even after Charles had been executed. Oddest of all were the coins of Scarborough in 1644–5, roughly

cut from silver plate, weighed and then accordingly marked with the precise value in shillings and pence below an image of the castle.

Up to the early 17th century all English coins were struck in precious metals, but as the value of the penny fell in real terms it became uneconomic to mint coins smaller than a halfpenny in silver. In 1616 James I granted a monopoly to the Duke of Richmond to strike copper farthings. This system of privatising the subsidiary coinage continued under Charles I, but under the Commonwealth copper farthings were struck by the Mint and this set the precedent for the tin and copper coins produced after the Restoration, the Duchess of Richmond (a mistress of Charles II) serving as the model for Britannia. A reluctance to mint base metal coins for small change, especially in the reign of George III when none was produced between 1775 and 1797, led to the proliferation of unofficial tokens issued by merchants and tavern-keepers.

Soon after the Restoration, the coinage of England was completely overhauled. The regular use of machinery for coin production from then onwards resulted in coins of an even diameter and thickness while an edge inscription DECUS ET TUTAMEN (an ornament and a safeguard) solved the age-old problem of clipping. In 1696 all the badly worn and clipped coins still in circulation were called in, melted down and a vast amount of new coinage produced, entailing the temporary re-opening of branch mints at Bristol, Chester, Exeter, Norwich and York for this purpose, their coins being indicated by initial letters below the king's bust.

The coinage in use in the late 17th and 18th centuries was based on the gold guinea, its multiples (up to five guineas) and its sub-divisions. It derived its name from Guinea on the West African coast whence much of the gold was imported. Coins were now regularly dated, but occasionally little symbols, known as provenance marks, indicated the source of the metal. Thus the elephant and castle denoted gold and silver supplied by the African Company. Originally tariffed at 20 shillings, the guinea eventually rose as high as 30 shillings due to fluctuations in the value of gold and silver, before settling at 21 shillings. Long after it had been replaced by the sovereign of 20 shillings in 1816, the guinea survived as money of account till the advent of decimalisation in 1971.

Provenance marks were extended in the 18th century. Coins of Queen Anne marked VIGO were struck from the bullion seized from the Spaniards during the Anglo-Dutch attack on Vigo Bay in 1702. Similarly coins of George II were marked LIMA in 1745–6 to denote the bullion seized from the Spaniards off the Peruvian coast in 1744 during Anson's voyage round the world. Other marks include the initials of the East India Company. Coins marked W.C.C. indicated silver supplied by the Welsh Copper Company, while those with roses and the Prince of Wales's feathers alternating in the angles of the shields on the reverse, denoted silver supplied by the Company for Smelting Pit Coale and Sea Coale (sic). Highly prized are the coins with the initials S.S.C. from silver supplied by the South Seas Company, most notorious of the boom and bust companies in the whole of English financial history.

Silver was only coined sporadically as the 18th century progressed, owing to a shortage of the metal, and for this reason small gold coins, such as the third and quarter guineas, were struck to fill the gap. The situation deteriorated during the French Revolutionary and Napoleonic Wars when gold itself was in short supply. To fill the gap Spanish dollars and half-dollars were countermarked with a bust of George III and put into circulation. The Bank of England also countermarked dollars with the effigy of Britannia (1804–11) for use as crowns (5 shillings) and also produced a range of smaller silver tokens ranging from 9d to 3s.

This was also the period when the silver penny and twopence vanished from everyday use, although they continued to be struck annually for use in the Royal Maundy ceremony. Prior to that time the little leather pouches containing coins doled out to deserving paupers on Maundy Thursday by the monarch, to the number of men and women equal to the years in the sovereign's age, consisted of the ordinary coins made up of 1d, 2d, 3d and 4d, and it is only since the late-18th century that special silver coins of these denominations have been produced.

For everyday circulation the silver penny and twopence were replaced by large copper coins. Because these coins had to have an intrinsic value equal to their face value, at a time when copper was worth a penny an ounce, it followed that these coins weighed 1 and 2 ounces respectively. Their cumbrous weight, together with their raised rims, led to them being nick-named the Cartwheel coinage. Too heavy for practical purposes they soon vanished from the scene. The twopence was scrapped but copper pennies were re-introduced in 1806, reduced to a much more manageable weight and size. The spasmodic appearance of copper halfpence and farthings (confined to 1799 and 1806–7) led to a resurgence of tradesmen's tokens which were not suppressed until the Mint resumed production of farthings in 1821, followed by pennies and halfpennies in 1825.

The Cartwheel coins were struck by Boulton and Watt at the Soho Mint, Birmingham, the first time that British coins were produced outside the Royal Mint, mainly because the Soho Mint was equipped with steam-powered machinery. A decade later this technology was embraced by the Royal Mint which then moved out of the Tower of London into new premises on Tower Hill nearby. This enabled it to cope with the great recoinage of 1816–20. After years of muddling through with inadequate resources and seldom producing sufficient coins for public use, the Mint embarked on a complete reform of the coins.

The guinea was scrapped and replaced by the sovereign worth 20 shillings. In the new gold and silver coinage the intrinsic value was much less than the face value, and this did away with the age-old problems that arose every time the value of gold or silver rose or fell. The coinage system of 1816 remained in use till 1971, the only changes in the intervening period being the switch from copper to bronze for the penny, halfpenny and farthing (1860) and the debasement of the silver coinage from sterling (.925 fine) to .500 fine (1920). The Maundy coins were similarly debased at that time but when .500 silver was replaced by cupro-nickel in 1947, sterling silver was re-introduced for the Maundy money, as well as proof versions of crowns.

The first half of the 19th century was the great era of Benedetto Pistrucci who created the neo-classical figure of St George slaying the dragon which formed the reverse motif of the gold coins and the silver crowns, and continues to this day on the sovereign series. The finest portraiture of the period was the work of William Wyon who produced the effigies of George III, George IV and William IV as well as the Young Head profile of Queen Victoria. The 'bun' portrait introduced for the bronze coins, was the work of Leonard Charles Wyon. Joseph Edgar Boehm sculpted the crowned bust used for the Jubilee coinage of 1887 and Thomas Brock the Veiled Head used for the coinage from 1893 till the end of Victoria's long reign.

There were several changes in the Victorian coinage, the most notable being the introduction of the florin in 1849. Worth two shillings or a tenth of a pound, it was the first step towards a decimal currency, although 120 years would elapse before decimalisation was actually accomplished. The other innovation was short-lived; as part of the Jubilee series of 1887 a double-florin (4 shillings) was introduced, but it was unpopular and discontinued three years later.

Although the so-called Jubilee series was launched in the year of Queen Victoria's Golden Jubilee it was intended for permanent use. The first true commemorative coin was not released until 1935, when a crown celebrated the Silver Jubilee of George V. The reverse showed an updated version of St George and the Dragon in the Art Deco style. Significantly, when a crown was produced in 1951 to mark the Festival of Britain, it reverted to Pistrucci's timeless version.

Heraldry continued to dominate the coinage reverses till the 1930s, but a portent of things to come was the issue of threepence and sixpence coins in the closing years of George V's reign, with reverses showing three and six acorns respectively. This concept would have continued in the coinage of Edward VIII with three or six interlocking rings. Pictorial motifs for the base-metal coins (including a 12-sided threepenny in nickel-brass) were essayed at the same time and featured three thrift flowers (3d), Drake's ship *Golden Hind* (halfpenny) and a wren (farthing), while the penny was redesigned to include the Eddystone Lighthouse in the background to Britannia. These designs were promptly adopted for the George VI coinage released in 1937. Another innovation was the introduction of two different shillings, one of which had Scottish motifs in deference to the Scottish ancestry of Queen Elizabeth.

Over the centuries there had been many changes in the Latin styles and titles of the reigning monarch inscribed on the obverse of the coinage, ranging from the 'King of England and France and Lord of Ireland' on Tudor coinage and the references to Great Britain in the coinage of James I, to the string of abbreviations on the coins of the first Hanoverian kings, alluding to their European titles. There were also additions to the coats of arms to take account of the Continental possessions of William of Orange and the Electors of Hanover. These were swept aside following the accession of Queen Victoria in 1837, but in the course of her long reign there were other changes in the inscription that reflected her role as Empress of India. The coins of Edward VII added BRITT. OMN to signify that he was King of All the Britains (i.e. the dominions and colonies as well as the United Kingdom). After the Indian sub-continent gained its independence in 1947 the reference to Emperor of India (IND. IMP.) was dropped, and finally, in 1954 the present Queen dispensed with BRITT. OMN., reflecting the change from the British Empire to the modern Commonwealth.

In the 1960s the Royal Mint transferred its operations to Llantrisant in South Wales and closed down its minting facility in London. This coincided with the abandonment of the £sd system and the introduction of the pound of 100 pence (1968–71). Although the circulating coinage is made of base alloys, there has been a tendency to use gold and silver for commemorative coins in more recent years. At the same time the frequency of commemoratives has accelerated. In addition to crowns (originally tariffed at five shillings or 25 pence but latterly £5), the Royal Mint has struck 50p and £2 commemoratives.

As part of the decimal series a seven-sided 50p coin was introduced, replacing the 10 shilling note. Originally the decimal coins were inscribed NEW PENCE, but in 1982 the word NEW was dropped. In the same year a small, seven-sided 20p was added to the series. A pound coin was adopted in 1983 and struck in aluminium-bronze. £2 coins in the same alloy were introduced in 1986 but confined to commemoratives and it was not until 1997 that a bimetallic £2 coin was produced for everyday circulation. In the same period the decimal halfpenny (worth 1.2 old pence) was dropped in 1984, a casualty of inflation. When decimal currency was adopted, the existing sixpence, shilling and florin were retained. Many slot machines and parking meters used sixpences, now regarded as 2½p coins, but after a few years it was quietly phased out. The shilling and florin, however, were the same weight and specification as the 5p and 10p respectively and were allowed to remain in circulation until substantially reduced in size in 1990–2, the 50p following suit in 1997.

Apart from the enormous changes in the circulating coinage, the past two decades have witnessed a tremendous upsurge in the issue of commemorative coins. In the same period we have seen the arrival of the Britannia series of bullion coins (£10, £25, £50 and £100 in gold), introduced in 1987, followed by the £1 and £2 in 1997, respectively containing half an ounce and one ounce of pure silver.

In the half century since Queen Elizabeth came to the throne, her effigy on the obverse has been updated from the original bust by Mary Gillick (1953–70), to those sculpted by Arnold Machin (1971–84), Raphael Maklouf (1985–92) and Ian Rank- Broadley (since 1998).

Separate issues of coins were made in Scotland from the early 12th century until 1707 when the Edinburgh Mint closed down, following the Act of Union. Irish coins date from the Hiberno-Norse pennies minted in Dublin about 995 to 1823, when the last coins were phased out as a result of the admission of Ireland into the United Kingdom in 1801. Distinctive coins were resumed by the Irish Free State in 1928 and continue in the Republic to this day, Euro coins with the harp emblem being introduced in 2001. Distinctive series of coins are issued in Guernsey, Jersey and the Isle of Man. In each case, separate series of coins were issued in earlier centuries, and the Channel Islands continued to have their own low-denomination coins, but since the advent of decimalisation in 1971 all three offshore islands have produced the full range of coins, including gold and silver. For further details, see the notes at the beginning of the relevant sections of this catalogue.

COLLECTING COINS

Coin collecting is one of the few acquisitive hobbies that can be pursued at little or no cost. At its most basic, anyone's pocket or purse may contain the beginnings of a collection. You can confine your interests to the current coins which you pick up in change. Of course, British coins are not as exciting nowadays as they were back in the late 1960s when decimalisation was imminent and everyone got the change-checkers' craze. This arose as a result of publicity surrounding the changeover and stories in the national press about coins from 1816 onwards still being valid and occasionally turning up in change. Indeed, it was not uncommon up to that time to find a George III 'Bullneck' shilling or an Edwardian 'Standing Britannia' florin in change, despite the fact that, ever since cupro-nickel replaced silver in the circulating coinage, more and more of the pre-1920 coins were being quietly taken out of circulation and melted down for their scrap value which far exceeded their face value.

The large bronze pennies and halfpennies which had been in use since 1860 were extremely popular because not only had they been minted in almost every year for over a century, but they also yielded interesting varieties such as those with the KN and H marks of the Kings Norton and Heaton mints of Birmingham to whom the Royal Mint had occasionally sub-contracted the work. And this attention to dates and marks paid off sometimes, as when someone found a half-crown dated 1952. Theroetically half-crowns had not been struck that year, yet here was an example which bore all the usual signs of having passed through countless hands, unrecognised for the great rarity that it was.

Relying on the coins picked up in change, however, may tell you a great deal about the money actually in circulation, but it will never lead to a comprehensive collection. The best, and easiest, way to collect contemporary British coins, as well as those of Ireland and the off-shore islands, is to subscribe to a new issue service run by the various mints and numismatic bureaux. That way you can be certain of keeping up with the latest issues.

It is no longer sufficient for the Royal Mint to produce coins for general circulation. In addition to attractively packaged year sets and sou-venir folders for each commemorative set in specimen condition, there are de luxe proofs, often struck in gold or silver. Prices for such collector's pieces range from a few pounds upwards and it is a hobby that can be pursued at different levels and price ranges.

Of course, this system only applies to contemporary coins, and if you wish to extend your collection backwards in time you will have to resort to a coin dealer or attend coin auctions. You can decide to specialise in certain denominations, such as shillings or sixpences, and try to track down examples of every reign, date and variety, or (if you can afford it) you might wish to concentrate on the coins of your own country, such as Scotland or Ireland or the Channel Islands. Collectors in England can even concentrate on the coins struck from Anglo-Saxon times till 1696 at the mints established in towns in their own county or region. At the top end of the range, there are the rare and very expensive coins produced at various Royalist mints during the Civil War and even the siege pieces from Carlisle, Newark, Pontefract and Scarborough. There are also many who now collect the very prolific trade tokens of the 17th to 19th centuries, particularly those of their own town or county.

Relatively few dealers now operate shop premises but many of them take part in the various fair circuits which enable customers to browse through their stock. In Britain the premier show is COINEX, held over the second weekend each October at the Marriott Hotel, London and organised by the BNTA. In recent years regional fairs have been organised by the BNTA in the north of England and South Wales in an attempt to bring the numismatic mainstream to collectors in the provinces. Other major events are the Irish Coin Show, held in Dublin each February and the Coin and Stamp Fairs held twice a year (January and July) at York Racecourse, but there are also various fair circuits which tour the country regularly. These are much smaller events, with anything between a dozen and 30 dealers on average, but they offer a convenient method of bringing the trade to collectors in many towns where there are no full-time dealers. Details of these fairs and their venues will be found in *Coin News* each month.

Many other dealers operate their business solely or mainly by mail order and publish monthly or quarterly lists which they send out to their regular clients. These lists range from the prestigious *Spink's Numismatic Circular*, published ten times a year and containing useful features as well as the latest offers, to duplicated sheets produced by many of the smaller dealers. Apart from dealers who cater to a very wide clientele, there are many specialists who concentrate on a particular area or period, such as Celtic coins, medieval hammered pennies, Maundy money and modern proof commemoratives.

The newcomer to the hobby is often worried about approaching a dealer who is less than fair in both buying and selling coins. How can he be sure that what the dealer is offering is genuine and not a fake or forgery? How can he be sure that the coin is actually of the grade advertised? How can he be sure that the price asked is a fair one? Of course the prices given in this catalogue are a guide, but it must be remembered that there are many imponderable factors governing the selling price of coins, that this can do no more than give a rough idea to coins in average condition. One guarantee of fair dealing and professional conduct is membership of one or other of the major trade bodies, the British Numismatic Trade Association and the International Association of Professional Numismatists. Details of members of the BNTA and IAPN can be obtained by contacting their respective secretaries, Mrs Carol Carter, PO Box 33, Hayling Island, Hampshire PO11 9WF (tel/fax: 023 9246 3131) and Jean-Luc Van der Scheuren, 14 rue de la Bourse, B-1000, Brussels, Belgium (tel: 0032 25 13 3400 or fax: 0032 25 13 2528). Not all reputable dealers, however, belong to these trade bodies. Many of them are every bit as professional in dealing with customers but prefer to pursue an independent course. In such cases advice from members of your local coin club (see below) will prove invaluable.

Apart from the dealers advertising in this catalogue, an obvious place to look for coin dealers in your locality is in the Yellow Pages directory, but much more effective will be to purchase *Coin News* (monthly from Token Publishing and available through your local newsagent or branch of WH Smith). This magazine also gives up-to-the-minute details of forthcoming auctions as well as reviews of recent sales which will help to give you an idea of the market and its scope.

There are four major salerooms in the London area holding sales of coins at regular intervals. Baldwin's are not only one of the largest dealers but also hold regular sales, both general and specialised, at 11 Adelphi Terrace. Bonhams now incorporates Glendinings, once the top auction house for coins, with premises at 101 New Bond Street. Dix Noonan Webb (established in 1991) at 16 Bolton Street, Piccadilly hold frequent sales at the New Connaught Rooms, Covent Garden. Sotheby's used to hold coin sales in their own right but these sales are now conducted in association with Sotheby's by Morton & Eden of 45 Maddox Street, the sales taking place at Sotheby's Conduit Street Gallery. Spink (founded in 1666) now covers a wide range of collectables, but holds three coin sales a year at 69 Southampton Row, Bloomsbury, generally in March, July and November. Outside London the main coin sales are conducted by Croydon Coin Auctions and Format of Birmingham, while Whyte's of Dublin are the leading saleroom in Ireland.

Coin News also contains a calendar of the meetings of the various numismatic societies and coin clubs throughout the United Kingdom. These notes give details of the venue and dates as well as the subjects of talks and other activities. The telephone number of the club secretary is also listed so it is a very easy matter to make contact and then go along to meetings. There is no substitute for the personal contact. Apart from the very wide range of topics covered in the syllabus, with something to suit all tastes, club meetings provide a great opportunity to meet fellow collectors, to swap coins and take part in the club auctions which usually offer a great deal of material at a very modest price, the ideal way for the beginner to build a collection.

Most coin clubs are affiliated to the British Association of Numismatic Societies. An enquiry to P.H. Mernick, the BANS secretary (42 Campbell Road, London E8 4DT, tel: 020 8980 5672 or e-mail: bans@mernicks.com) will put you in touch with a club near you. BANS also have an excellent and informative website: www.coinclubs.freeserve.co.uk

CARE AND CONSERVATION

A golden rule in coins as in every other form of collectable is always to buy the best you can afford, but there is no point in spending large sums of money in selecting the best coins if you do not look after them properly and maintain them in the condition in which you purchased them. Although some coins minted more than 2000 years ago are still available in virtually mint state, proving the indestructibility of gold and silver, nevertheless there are problems to solve and pitfalls to watch out for, in keeping your treasures in the best possible condition. Accommodating your coins is the biggest problem of all, so it is very important to give a lot of thought to this.

Traditionally collectors housed their coins in specially designed cabinets and this is still the best method, although it is also the most expensive. Because of acids in many types of timber which might react with coins, such cabinets should only be made of air-dried mahogany, walnut or rosewood, never oak, cedar or any highly resinous timber such as pine, because these woods can badly tarnish coins. Coin cabinets contain shallow drawers holding trays of the same wood, with half-drilled holes of various diameters appropriate to different sizes of coins. The holes are usually lined with green baize and traditionally collectors wrote the details of each coin on a small paper disc, such as a brief description and perhaps the date of purchase and the price paid. Such cabinets usually have double doors fitted with locks and are often very attractive pieces of furniture which themselves fetch high prices when they turn up in the saleroom.

Fortunately there are modern equivalents that, being mass-produced, are much cheaper and do the job perfectly well. These are cases containing felt-lined plastic trays with compartments to fit every size of coin. Not only are these cases relatively inexpensive but they also provide a convenient means of transporting coins and are thus very popular with dealers attending coin fairs. Another method is to store coins in chemically inert manila envelopes which stand upright in narrow cases. The salient details of each coin can be written on the envelope. This is the cheapest method but it has the disadvantage that the coins are not readily apparent, unlike the trays where you can see your coins at a glance.

There are also various types of album, but they should be treated with extreme caution. Back in the late 1960s when the boom in coin-collecting took off, several firms produced albums containing PVC sleeves which had small pockets tailored to the main coin sizes. The sleeves were slotted into sturdy binders and had the merit of being both inexpensive and compact, as several albums could stand side by side on a bookshelf. The immediate failing of these albums was that when the sleeves were filled with coins they tended to sag under the weight, and eventually pulled away from the binder. More seriously, a chemical reaction occurred when the PVC came in contact with coins. Silver coins turned a strange golden colour, but bronze and cupronickel coins turned green or produced a strange yellowish slime which was very difficult to eradicate.

Things have moved on considerably since that time, but collections still turn up in albums of this sort and exhibit the harmful effects of polyvinyl chloride. Modern coin albums have overcome the problems and drawbacks of the earlier types, in that their pages are made of a rigid, chemically inert plastic and have much stronger posts securing them to the binders. Furthermore, the best type has separate strips for each row of coins and these are then inserted into horizontal sleeves so that the coins are doubly protected and not liable to fall out of their pockets if pages are turned over carelessly. Remember that coin albums, when full, are very heavy and best stored on steel shelving. Great care should be taken to ensure an even temperature and humidity and avoid exposure to strong sunlight.

CLEANING COINS

This is like matrimony – it should not be embarked on lightly. Indeed, the advice given by the magazine *Punch* in regard to marriage is equally sound in this case – don't do it! It is far better to have a dirty coin than an irretrievably damaged one. Every dealer has horror stories of handling coins that previous owners have 'improved' by cleaning, to their lasting detriment. The worst example consisted of coins dug out of the ground by a detectorist who enhanced his finds by buffing them with the sort of machine used by lapidaries to polish gemstones.

It is important to distinguish between grime (which should be removed) and patina, the protective layer of oxidation which is part of the charm of antique coins, ranging from the bluish tone on silver coins to the warm green hues found on copper. It would be monumental folly and vandalism of the worst kind to attempt to remove such patina with metal polish. On the other hand dirt which accumulates on coins which have been in general circulation, from the sweaty palms of countless transactions, is best removed. In most cases immersion in warm water containing a mild detergent (such as used in dish washing), with cotton buds or a very soft brush to dislodge stubborn dirt, will work wonders. Brushes should have animal bristles, never nylon or other artificial fibres. After cleaning, the coins should be rinsed well and then carefully dried with a soft cloth. More persistent cases may require a degreasing solvent. It was once reported that a well-known brand of sauce was very effective in removing grease from coins, but lighter fuel, applied with a soft cloth or cotton bud, is the simplest method. Gold coins can be cleaned with dilute citric acid (such as lemon juice) while silver is best washed in a solution of one part ammonia to ten parts warm water. Copper coins present the biggest problems, but grime and verdigris can be removed or at least mitigated by careful washing in a 20 per cent solution of sodium sesquicarbonate. Coins from the Second World War period were often made of cheaper alloys involving tin, zinc, iron or steel which has not worn too well, but they can be cleaned in a 5 per cent solution of caustic soda containing some aluminium or zinc foil or filings, but they must be rinsed well afterwards in clean water and carefully dried. There is now available a range of cleaning fluids suitable for gold, silver and base metal coins, which may be purchased from many coin dealers. It is important, however, to follow the instructions to the letter.

If cleaning should only be approached with the greatest trepidation, polishing is definitely out! Beginners sometimes fall into the appalling error of thinking that a smart rub with metal polish might improve the appearance of their coins. Short of actually punching a hole through it, there is no more destructive act. Polishing a coin may improve its superficial appearance for a few days, but such abrasive action will destroy the patina and reduce the fineness of the high points of the surface. Even if a coin is only polished once, it will never be quite the same again, and an expert can tell this a mile off.

Coins removed from the soil or the sea bed present special problems due to chemical reaction between the metals and the salts in the earth or sea water. In such cases, the best advice is to take them to the nearest museum and let the experts decide what can or should be done.

Coins should always be handled with the greatest care by holding the rims between forefinger and thumb. The acids and oils secreted by the fingers can leave indelible fingerprints on coins, so it is always advisable to wear a pair of fine silk or cotton gloves when handling specimens. Plastic tongs are available from coin dealers and are also very useful in handling coins although it takes some practice to use them with dexterity and there is always the risk that you might accidentally drop a coin on the table or floor, with disastrous results.

GRADING AND CONDITION

Condition is by far the most important factor in determining the value of a coin. Beginners are often surprised to discover that an enormous gap exists between a coin in flawless mint condition and one similar in every respect but showing marks of wear. Over the years collectors and dealers have evolved a system for grading coins. Altogether, there are about a dozen different grades, although for all practical purposes only the top four or five should be considered worth collecting, unless a coin is so rare that you would have to settle for something in poorer condition. Obviously Greek, Roman and medieval coins are usually encountered in the poorer grades, although it should be pointed out that really superlative examples do exist. At the other end of the spectrum modern coins are not worth bothering about unless they are in Extremely Fine (EF) condition or better. It goes without saying that present-day collectors' pieces and de luxe coins in proof or prooflike state can only be considered if they are in the most perfect condition. Anything less would not be acceptable.

Proof coins are generally struck several times to bring up the fine detail. Specially prepared dies are used for this purpose and the blanks are polished to a fine mirror quality. In many cases the high relief on proof coins is frosted to provide a greater contrast with the mirror background. Any edge knocks or scratches on the surface of such pieces would severely mark them down. Proofs are usually encased in felt or velvet lined boxes, and modern issues are often encapsulated in clear plastic for good measure in order to minimise wear.

Coins produced for general circulation, on the other hand, are struck on high-speed presses and tumble into a hopper and are then bagged up for despatch to banks. It follows that a certain amount of minor scratches or other blemishes are inevitable. The aim of the collector should be to secure examples in as near perfect condition as humanly possible

Apart from proofs, the various grades of condition that the collector will encounter in auction catalogues and dealers' lists are as follows:

Fleur de coin (abbreviated as FDC) is synonymous with **Brilliant Uncirculated** (B.U. or B. Unc.). This is the state that proofs should be in,

but it also includes prooflike coins (usually struck to a higher standard than ordinary coins, often with a high polish overall). This includes so-called specimen coins, now produced by the Royal Mint and sold in presentation folders.

Uncirculated (Unc) is the highest grade normally applied to a coin struck by standard minting equipment. A bronze penny in this grade should have the brilliant golden-red lustre that distinguishes newly minted coins. With age, this tends to darken attractively as the coin acquires a patina. This is caused by atmospheric oxidation and is, in reality a form of protective rust, but on no account should any attempt be made to remove it by polishing. Such action would utterly destroy its value as a collectable. In uncirculated coins even the finest detail, such as the Queen's hair, should be sharply defined. Anything that slightly falls below this is often described as **About Uncirculated** (A.U.).

Extremely Fine (E.F.) denotes a coin that is in a state of almost pristine perfection but has been handled to some degree. It is probably the finest condition that older coins are likely to possess. It should have every detail of the engraving clearly delineated but will probably have lost some of its original lustre. In addition you will sometimes come across 'Good E.F.' or 'E.F. Plus' meaning that the coin belongs towards the upper end of the spectrum but is not quite good enough to qualify as Uncirculated.

Very Fine (V.F.) coins will have slight traces of wear on their higher surfaces. Points to watch for are the fine lines in the hair of the portrait or signs of wear on the truncation of the bust, the highest point of the obverse. Coins in V.F. condition are collectable only if no better specimens are easily obtainable. You will sometimes see coins described as 'about E.F.' or about V.F., implying a subtle shading of difference and perhaps a slightly lower standard. Coins described as 'E.F./V.F.' have one side in better condition than the other, although any lessening of standards on one side must inevitably affect their overall quality.

Below V.F. coins are not really worth bothering about unless they are scarce in any case. Dealers do not usually handle modern coins in any lower grades (unless they are very rare), but when it comes to old coins lower standards are often acceptable, owing to their scarcity in the better grades. Thus, if you collect classical or medieval coins you will often have to settle for poorer condition. The following definitions should be useful when considering older material.

Fine (F.) describes a coin with extensive signs of wear. To the untrained eye it may look perfectly all right, but when you examine it closely under a magnifying glass you will see that the higher points of the design are smoother and less well-defined than they should be, while the lettering is thicker and coarser as a result of constant handling.

Very Good (V.G.) is a euphemism that, like modern coinage, has become so debased that it now means rather bad! On such a coin only a small fraction of the finer detail would have survived while the portions in high relief, as well as the lettering, would be quite blurred.

Good (G.) now means the exact opposite. A coin in this condition would be worn smooth all over. The date would be just legible and no more, and for this reason collectors will occasionally keep a coin in such bad condition when a particular year is scarce.

Below this grade come **Fair**, **Mediocre** and **Poor**, terms that have become so abused in practice as to be virtually synonymous, although Poor is generally reserved for coins that are damaged as well as worn, either clipped or pierced. Coins have frequently been converted into jewellery, hence the piercing, but almost as bad are coins showing traces of solder or claw marks where they have been mounted into rings and brooches; such blemishes detract from their numismatic value. Surprisingly enough, many modern coins show extensive surface marking as a result of being used constantly in parking meters and payphones.

Slabbing

It will soon be apparent that the various terms described above tend to be subjective and open to individual interpretation. In a bid to overcome such imprecise terms and adopt a more scientific approach the American Numismatic Association has devised a system which will eventually render the terms used in Britain obsolete, and already many dealers in the United Kingdom have adopted them. This system divides proofs and uncirculated coins into ten grades (five for each category):

Proof-70 Perfect Proof
Proof-67 Gem Proof
Proof-65 Choice Proof
Proof-63 Select Proof
Proof-60 Proof
MS-70 Mint State Perfect condition
MS-67 Gem
MS-65 Choice
MS-63 Select
MS-60 Uncirculated

Below 60, numbers 1 to 59 indicate the various degrees of wear:

AU-55 Choice About Uncirculated
AU-50 About Uncirculated
EF-45 Choice Extremely Fine
EF-40 Extremely Fine
VF-30 Choice Very Fine
VF-20 Very Fine
F-12 Fine
VG-8 Very Good
G-4 Good
AG-4 About Good
BS-1 Basal State

The term 'slabbing' describes the practice, which originated in the USA, of selling coins encapsulated in cards with circular plastic windows on both sides. The full details of the coin are printed on the card, together with its grading number. The intention is that such coins, once 'slabbed' and correctly graded by experts, should remain in that form for ever more. Needless to say, this system has had a mixed reception in Europe and many collectors in Britain prefer to collect coins in the traditional manner that enables them to examine and handle their specimens more closely.

COIN TERMS

The following terms are frequently encountered in auction catalogues and dealers' lists and are used in this catalogue.

Ae (Latin *Aes*, bronze) coins of brass, bronze or copper.

Alloy Mixture of metals used for coins.

Aluminium-bronze Alloy of aluminium and copper used in the gold-coloured £1 and £2 coins.

Ar (Latin *Argentum*, silver) coins of silver.

Au (Latin *Aurum*, gold) coins of gold.

Bag mark Minor scratch found on otherwise uncirculated coins, due to coins clashing in the mint bags on their way to the banks.

Barbarous Crude imitation of Greek or Roman coins produced by the Celtic tribes.

Base Non-precious metals used in subsidiary coinage and all modern circulating coins.

Bath Metal Poor-quality bronze alloy produced in Bath and used for Irish and American tokens in the 18th century.

Beading Ornament in the form of beads or dots on the rim of a coin.

Billon Inferior alloy containing a small quantity of silver mixed with copper or tin.

Bi-metallic Coins struck in two separate metals or alloys. First used by Italy (1982) but now employed for the £2 coins using a cupro-nickel centre and an outer ring of aluminium-bronze.

Blank Piece of metal on which a coin is struck. Sometimes referred to as a flan or planchet.

Blundered inscription Wording on a coin in which the letters are jumbled or reversed, or almost meaningless, reflecting the illiteracy of the minter, especially in Celtic coins.

Bonnet piece Scottish gold coin (1539–40) showing King James V wearing a large flat bonnet.

Box coin Circular container, usually made from Cartwheel coins hollowed out and screwed together to form a box for paper discs of a commemorative nature.

Brass Alloy of copper and zinc, first used in Britain for the 3d coins of 1937. See also Aluminium-bronze.

Breeches Money Nickname for the coins of the Commonwealth showing conjoined oval shields of England and Scotland, resembling a pair of breeches.

Brockage A mis-struck coin with the design normal on one side and incuse on the other, caused by a previously struck coin adhering to the die and thus transferring the image in reverse to the next coin to pass through the press.

Bronze Alloy of copper and tin, adopted in Britain for the subsidiary coinage from 1860 onwards.

Bull Neck Nickname for the last coinage of George III, (1816–17).

Bullion Precious metals (silver, gold or platinum) in ingots, bars or scrap, before being melted down and converted into coins.

Bullion coins Coins struck in precious metals and marked not with a denomination so much as the weight and fineness of the metal content, so that it may be traded at the prevailing price on the bullion market. Coins in this category include the Krugerrand and the Canadian Maple Leaf as well as the Angel and Noble (Isle of Man) and Britannia coinage of the UK.

Bun Coinage Coins of 1860–94 showing Queen Victoria with her hair in a bun.

Carat Originally a unit of weight for precious stones, it also signifies the fineness or purity of gold, being 1/24th of the whole. Thus 9 carat gold is .375 fine and 22 carat (the British sovereign standard) is .916. Medieval English gold coins were struck in almost pure gold (23.5 carat) while some modern gold coins are virtually 24 carat (.9999 fine), sometimes called 'four nines gold'.

Cartwheel Nickname for the large and cumbersome penny and twopence of 1797, on account of their size and the heavy rims bearing the inscriptions.

Cased Set Set of coins in proof or mint condition, prepared for sale to collectors.

Cast coins Coins cast from molten metals in moulds instead of being struck from blanks. This method was used to produce the Manx coinage of 1709.

Clad Coins Coins with a core of one metal covered with a layer of another. British 1p and 2p coins, formerly made of bronze, have actually been made of stainless steel since 1992, with a copper cladding. Such coins are attracted to a magnet.

Clash Mark Mirror image found on coins struck from a pair of dies which have suffered damage as a result of being accidentally struck together without a blank between them.

Clipping Dishonest practice of slicing off slivers of gold or silver from coins, these parings being then hoarded and traded for cash. Clipped coins were thus below the legal weight and eventually had to be melted down and recoined, at a loss to the revenue. This practice was suppressed in 1662 when milled coins, with an edge inscription, were introduced.

Coin Piece of metal stamped with a device and issued by authority of the government for circulation as money.

Commemorative Coin issued to mark a historic anniversary or a current event and generally on sale for a limited period.

Conjoined Term describing overlapping profiles or busts on a coin.

Copper Metal (denoted by the abbreviation *Cu*) used for subsidiary coinage, often alloyed with tin to form bronze, or zinc to produce brass. An alloy in which a large proportion of copper is used with silver is known as billon.

Coppernose Nickname for debased silver shillings of Henry VIII, struck mainly in copper with a thin wash of silver which soon wore off the highest point of the obverse, the King's nose.

Counterfeit Imitation of a coin intended for general circulation, to deceive the public and defraud the revenue.

Crown Originally a gold coin, introduced in 1526 and worth 5 shillings, but later struck in silver. Not too practical in general circulation because of its size but very popular as a medium for commemorative coins. Retained since 1971, first as a 25p coin but now tariffed at £5.

Crown Gold Gold of 22 carat (.916) fineness, so-called because it was first used for the gold crown of 1526 and the standard fineness for British gold ever since.

Cupro-nickel (abbreviation *Cu-Ni*) Alloy of copper and nickel used mainly as a substitute for silver in British coins since 1947.

Debasement Reduction in the precious metal content of the coinage, practised in Tudor times and, more recently, in the British coinage, reduced from .925 to .500 fine silver in 1920 and then to cupro-nickel in 1947.

Decimalisation Switch from £sd to the pound of 100 new pence, instituted in 1968 and completed in 1971.

Demonetisation Withdrawal of coins from circulation and declaring them to be no longer legal tender (e.g. the penny and half-crown in 1971, as they did not fit into the decimal system).

Device Heraldic term for the motif on coins.

Die Hardened piece of steel bearing the mirror image of the device to be struck on one side of a coin.

Dodecagonal Greek for twelve-sided, applied to the nickel-brass threepenny introduced in 1937.

Ecclesiastical Coins Coins struck in the Middle Ages by a religious authority, such as the Archbishops of Canterbury and York, the Bishop of Durham and even the Abbot of Reading.

Edge Inscription Lettering or ornament on the edge of a coin originally to prevent clipping. Occasionally commemorative (e.g. the Festival of Britain crown, 1951) but nowadays purely decorative, in conjunction with graining, on the £1 and £2 coins.

Effigy Image of a person, usually a profile or bust but occasionally a three-quarter or facing portrait, occupying the obverse or 'heads' side of a coin.

Engrailing Technical term for the close serrations round the edge of a coin, applied as a security device to prevent clipping.

Engraving Art of cutting lines or grooves in a die used for striking coins.

Error Mistake made in the design or production of a coin. Errors of design include blundered inscriptions. Errors in production include using the wrong obverse and reverse dies, thus creating a mule, or the wrong collar (e.g. a scalloped edge normally used for Hong Kong dollars, applied to British 10p coins).

Exergue Lower segment of a coin, usually divided from the rest of the field by a horizontal line and usually containing the date, value or ornament.

Facing Portrait on a coin facing to the front instead of the side (profile).

Field Flat part of a coin between the legend, the effigy and the raised parts of the design.

Fillet Heraldic term for the ribbon or headband on the effigy of the ruler (e.g. Queen Victoria).

Flan Alternative term for blank or planchet.

Forgery Imitation of a coin intended to deceive collectors (as opposed to a counterfeit intended to pass as current coin).

Frosting Matt surface used for the high relief

areas on many proof coins.

Ghost Faint image of the design on one side of a coin visible on the other, as shown on the halfpenny and penny of George V (1911–27).

Godless Florin Two-shilling coin of 1849 in which the abbreviation D.G. (*Dei Gratia*, 'by the Grace of God') was omitted.

Gold Precious metal (abbreviation *Au*) used as a coinage medium since the 7th century BC. It was used for general circulation in the United Kingdom till 1914 but since then has been confined to bullion and coins aimed at the numismatic market.

Gothic Crown Nickname for the crowns issued in 1847–53 on account of the script employed.

Grain Weight of a single grain of wheat and the smallest unit of weight in Britain. The troy grain was 1/5760 of a pound, used in the weighing of precious metals and retained in numismatics for weighing coins. A grain is 1/480 troy ounce (0.066 gram in the metric system).

Graining Term denoting the reeded edge on milled coins.

Gun Money Emergency coinage of Ireland (1689–91) struck from gunmetal during a shortage of silver.

Hammered Term denoting coins produced by the traditional manner of striking a blank laid on an anvil with a hammer. Hammered coins are generally uneven in shape and thickness, factors which tended to encourage clipping. They survived in Britain till 1662.

Hat Piece Alternative name for the Bonnet Piece of James VI of Scotland, 1591.

Holed Term applied to a coin which has been pierced for suspension round the neck as a form of jewellery or talisman (e.g. the gold angel).

Hybrid Alternative name for a mule.

Incuse Impression which cuts into the surface of a coin, e.g. the inscriptions on the Cartwheel coins of 1797 or the 20p coins since 1982.

Intrinsic Net metallic value of a coin as opposed to the nominal or face value.

Key Date The rarest date in a long-running series in which the dates are changed at annual intervals.

Laureate Term for a laurel wreath often enclosing an inscription or a shield, or adorning the temples of the ruler in the style of the Roman emperors.

Legal Tender Coin which is declared by law to be current money and which tradesmen and shopkeepers are obliged to accept in payment for goods and services.

Legend Inscription on a coin.

Long Cross Coinage Type of coinage introduced by Henry III in 1247, distinguished by the cross on the reverse extending to the edge as a precaution against clipping. This style was retained for the silver coins till Tudor times.

Lustre Sheen or bloom on the surface of an uncirculated coin.

Matt Finely granulated surface or overall satin finish, briefly fashionable in the early 1900s (e.g. the Edward VII proof set of 1902).

Maundy Money Set of small silver coins denominated 1, 2, 3 and 4 pence, distributed by the monarch to the poor on Maundy Thursday. The custom dates from the Middle Ages. Men and women, to the number of year's in the ruler's age, receive coins to that value in pence. It follows that the older the monarch the commoner the coins.

Milling Mechanical process of producing coins, as opposed to the hammered technique operated by hand. It takes its name from the water mills originally used to drive the machinery.

Mint Place where coins are struck. The term is often applied to coins in an uncirculated state.

Mint Set Set of coins in the package, folder or case issued by the mint.

Mintmark Device on a coin to denote the place of minting, (e.g. the letter E on coins struck at York or the letters KN used at the King's Norton Mint), it is also applied to the letter or symbol indicating the Trial of the Pyx and thus a rough method of dating coins before actual dates became the norm in the 17th century.

Mirror Finish Highly polished surface of proof coins.

Misstrike Coin in which the image is off-centre.

Modified Effigy Effigy which has been slightly altered in the course of a coin series, such as the minor changes in the Victorian Young Head and Old Head effigies and the George V profile of 1926–7 intermediate between the original large and later small profiles.

Mule Coin whose obverse is not matched with its official or regular reverse.

Nickel Metallic element (symbol *Ni*), a hard white metal extensively used as a cheap substitute for silver, and usually alloyed with copper.

Obsidional Currency Term (from Latin *obsidium*, siege) applied to the makeshift coins produced by the Royalists besieged in Carlisle, Newark, Pontefract and Scarborough during the Civil War.

Obverse 'Heads' side of a coin, so-called because it bears the effigy of the reigning monarch.

Patina Oxidation forming on the surface of metals, e.g. the greenish tone on copper or the bluish tone on silver coins.

Pattern Trial piece for a coin, prepared by the mint while the design may be still at a preliminary stage and therefore differing from the coins actually issued. Mints often produce patterns when bidding for a coinage contract and they are of interest as examples of what might have been.

Pellet Raised circular ornament used as a spacing device in coin legends. Groups of pellets appear in the angles of the cross on the reverse of many silver pennies.

Piedfort Piece struck from coinage dies on a blank of twice or three times the normal weight and thickness. Originally made as presentation pieces in the Middle Ages, they are now produced for sale to collectors as a variant of proof coins.

Pile Lower die incorporating the obverse motif, as opposed to the trussel bearing the reverse image.

Planchet French term for a coin blank.

Platinum Precious metal (symbol *Pn*) with a higher specific gravity than gold and a harder, brighter surface than silver. Once regarded as worthless, it was mainly used in the counterfeiting of gold coins with a gold-plated finish, but was used briefly in Russia for 3, 6 or 12 rouble coins. In more recent years it has been a popular medium for limited edition proof coins, especially from the Isle of Man.

Plugged Coins Coins struck in one metal but containing a small plug of another. Farthings and halfpence of Charles II and James II (1684–7) were struck in tin with a copper plug as a security feature to defeat counterfeiters.

Potin French term for pewter, applied to the base alloy used by the Celtic tribes for coinage at the beginning of the Christian era.

Privy Mark Secret mark incorporated in the design of a coin to identify the minter or even the particular die used. The term is also used loosely to denote any small symbol or initials on a coin other than a mint mark.

Profile Side view of a face, widely used as a coinage effigy.

Proof Originally a trial strike to test the dies but now denoting a special collectors' version struck with specially polished dies on mirror blanks, and recognised by its high quality finish.

Provenance Mark Mark indicating the source of the metal, e.g. VIGO and LIMA on coins of 1702–3 and 1745–6 respectively or bearing the emblem or initials of one or other of the companies that supplied bullion to the Mint in the 18th century.

Pyx Box in which specimen coins were stored for the annual inspection known as the Trial of the Pyx. Many of the mintmarks on English coins of the 14th–17th centuries were in use from one trial to the next and thus form a chronological sequence.

Reeding Security edging on coins, comprising close vertical ridges.

Relief Raised parts of the coin, as opposed to incuse.

Restrike Coin produced from dies subsequent to the original use.

Reverse 'Tails' side of a coin, regarded as of lesser importance to the obverse.

Sceat (Anglo-Saxon word for treasure) applied to small silver coins about 20 grains in weight, on par with the Merovingian denier or penny. Introduced to England in the late 7th century but declined in weight and value about 760 and was eventually replaced by the penny.

Scyphate Coin with a concave flan (from Greek *scypha*, a skiff or small boat), widely used in Byzantine coinage but also used for the £2 coin celebrating the European Football Championship (1996), the curve simulating the surface of a football.

Short Cross Coinage Type of coinage introduced by Henry II in 1180 and struck till 1247 when it was replaced by the Long Cross type.

Silver Precious metal, chemical symbol Ag but denoted in numismatic shorthand as *Ar* (from Latin *Argentum*). Widely used as a coinage metal from the 6th century BC to the present day, although since the middle of the 20th century mainly confined to collector's editions and replaced in everyday use by cupro-nickel.

Spade Guinea Popular name for the guineas of George III (1787–99) on account of the spade-shaped shield on the reverse.

Specimen Term generally applied to a single coin but now more specifically used to denote a coin struck to a higher standard than general circulation requires, but not as high a quality as a proof.

Sterling Word denoting a standard weight and fineness and hence the more general meaning of recognised worth. It is believed to come from the Easterlings, German traders who settled in London in the 13th century and produced silver pennies of uniform fineness. Sterling silver is silver .925 fine.

Styca Name given to the debased silver sceats of Northumbria in the 8th century.

Thrymsa Early Anglo-Saxon gold coin derived from the Merovingian *tremissis* or third-solidus, current about 630–75.

Tin Metallic element, chemical symbol *St* (from Latin *Stannum*). Because it is unstable and corrodes readily it is unsuitable as a coinage medium on its own, although it was briefly used for farthings and halfpennies in the late 17th century. It is mainly alloyed with copper to produce bronze.

Token Piece of money whose nominal value is greater than its intrinsic value. Most British coins since 1816 fall into this category, but the term is restricted in numismatics to describe unofficial pieces, mostly issued by merchants and shopkeepers in times when there is a shortage of official coinage, e.g. from the late 17th to early 19th centuries. The term is also applied to the silver pieces issued by the Bank of England during the Napoleonic Wars.

Touchpiece Any coin kept as a lucky charm, but usually applied to the medieval gold angel worn round the neck as a cure for King's Evil (scrofula). For this reason many examples of this coin have been pierced.

Trade Coins Coins mainly intended for international trading purposes. Many British coins, from the medieval sterlings to the modern sovereigns, have been traded all over the world. Silver dollars intended specifically for overseas trade were minted from 1600 till the early 20th century.

Truncation Cut at the base of the profile or bust on a coin, sometimes containing a die number or the engraver's initials.

Trussel Reverse die in hammered coinage.

Type Chief motif on a coin, identifying the series.

Type Set Set of coins comprising one of each coin in a particular series, regardless of the actual dates of issue.

Uniface Coin having an image on one side only.

Variety Modification of a type, effigy or inscription.

Vis-à-vis (French for 'face to face') describing an obverse in which joint rulers are portrayed facing each other, e.g. English coins of Mary Tudor and Philip II and Scottish coins of Mary Queen of Scots and Henry Lord Darnley.

Wire Coin Nickname for a coin produced in the 18th century with exceptionally thin numerals of value.

Year Set Set of coins usually produced by the Mint containing specimens of the coins issued in a particular year.

Young Head Profile of Queen Victoria sculpted by William Wyon and used for the copper coins of 1837–60 and gold and silver till 1887.

Zinc Metallic element, symbol *Zn*, alloyed with copper to form brass.

RECOMMENDED READING

Angus, Ian, *Coins and Money Tokens*, Ward Lock, 1974

Bateson, Dr J.D. *Coinage in Scotland*, Spink, 1997

Bateson, Dr J.D. *Scottish Coins*, Shire Publications, 1987

Besly, Edward, *Coins and Medals of the English Civil War*, 1990

Blunt, C.ER. Stewart and Lyon, C.S.S. *Coinage in 10th Century England*, 1989

Bradley, H.W. *A Handbook of Coins of the British Isles*, Hale, 1984

Buck, I. *Medieval English Groats*, 2000

British Academy *Sylloge of Coins of the British Isles*, 50 vols.

Brooke, George C. *English Coins*, 1966

Coincraft *Standard Catalogue of English and U.K. Coins*, 1999–

Coincraft *Standard Catalogue of the Coins of Scotland, Ireland, Channel Islands and Isle of Man*, 1999.

Cooper, D. *Coins and Minting*, Shire Publications, 1996.

Cooper, D. *The Art and Craft of Coinmaking*, Spink, 1988

Dolley, Michael *Anglo-Saxon Pennies*, British Museum, 1970

Dowle, Anthony and Finn, Patrick *The Guide Book to the Coinage of Ireland*, 1969

Dyer, Graham P. *Royal Sovereign, 1489–1989*, Royal Mint, 1989

Dyer, Graham P. *The Royal Mint, an Illustrated History, Royal Mint*, 1986

Elias, E.R.D. *The Anglo-Gallic Coins*, 1984

Freeman, A. *The Moneyer and Mint in the Reign of Edward the Confessor, 1042–1066*, 1985

Grinsell, L.V. *The History and Coinage of the Bristol Mint*, Bristol Museum, 1985

Grueber, Harold A. *Handbook of the Coins of Great Britain and Ireland*, 1970

Hobbs, Richard. *British Iron Age Coins in the British Museum*, British Museum, 1996

Holmes, Nicholas, *Scottish Coins, a History of Small Change in Scotland*, National Museums of Scotland, 1998

De Jersey, Philip, *Celtic Coinage in Britain*, Shire Publications, 1996

Linecar, Howard W.A. *British Coin Designs and Designers*, Bell, 1977

Linecar, Howard W.A. *The Crown Pieces of Great Britain and the Commonwealth of Nations*, 1969

Linecar, Howard W.A., *The Milled Coinage of England, 1662–1946*, Spink, 1976

Linecar, H.W.A. and Stone, A.G. *English Proof and Pattern Crown-sized Pieces, 1658–1960*, 1968

Manville, Harrington E. *Tokens of the Industrial Revolution*, 1999

McCammon, A.L.T. *Currencies of the Anglo-Norman Isles*, Spink, 1984

Mackay, James, *A History of Modern English Coinage, Henry VII to Elizabeth II*, Longman, 1984

Mackay, James, *Coin Facts and Feats*, Seaby, 1990

Mackay, James, *Key Definitions in Numismatics*, Muller, 1982

Mackay, James, *The Beginner's Guide to Coin Collecting*, Apple Press, 1991

Mackay, James, *The Encyclopaedia of Isle of Man Coins and Tokens*, Pobjoy Mont, 1979–80

Mackay, James, *The Gold Sovereign*, Token Publishing, 2000

Mackay, James (ed.), *Coin Yearbook*, Token Publishing (annual, latest edition, 2004)

Mays, James O'Donald, *The Splendid Shilling*, New Forest Leaves, 1982

North, J.J. *English Hammered Coins*, 2 vols, 1993–4

O'Sullivan, W. *The Earliest Anglo-Irish Coinage*, Dublin, 1964

O'Sullivan, W. *The Earliest Irish Coinage*, Dublin, 1981

O'Sweeney, James, *A Numismatic History of the Birmingham Mint*, 1981

Peck, C. Wilson, *English Copper, Tin and Bronze Coins, 1558–1958*, British Museum, 1960

Rayner, Philip A. *English Silver Coins Since 1649*, Seaby, 1992

Reeds, Brian (ed.), *Coins of England and the United Kingdom*, Seaby, 1990

Robinson, Brian, *Silver Pennies & Linen Towels, the Story of the Royal Maundy*, Spink, 2003

Seaby, H.A. and Bussell, Margaret, *British Copper Coins and their Values*, Seaby, 1982

Stewart, Ian H. *The Scottish Coinage*, 1967

Sutherland, C.H.V. *English Coinage 600–1900*, Batsford, 1973

Van Arsdell, Richard D. *Celtic Coinage of Britain*, 1989

PUBLIC COLLECTIONS

Most museums in the British Isles have a coin collection, ranging from a general accumulation of representative world coins to highly specialised studies of local coinage, perhaps produced at a medieval mint or from a Royalist stronghold in the Civil War. Your local museum will tell you what material they possess and whether it is on public display or not. Below are listed the major national collections and more important provincial collections, in alphabetical order by town or city.

Aylesbury
Buckinghamshire County Museum, Church Street. Roman and hammered English coins and Buckinghamshire tokens. Tel: 01296 88849.

Bath
Roman Baths Museum, Pump Room. Roman coins. Tel: 01225 461111.

Batley
Bagshaw Museum and Art Gallery, Wilton Park. Roman, English, Scottish and Irish coins and Yorkshire tokens. Tel: 01924 472514.

Bedford
Bedford Museum, Castle Lane. Comprehensive collections of Roman, medieval and later English coins and tokens. Tel: 01234 353323.

Belfast
Ulster Museum, Botanic Gardens. Irish, English and British coins. Tel: 01232 381251.

Berwick
Berwick Borough Museum, The Clock Block, Berwick Barracks, Ravensdowne. Roman, Scottish and medieval English coins. Tel: 01289 330044.

Birmingham
City Museum and Art Gallery, Chamberlain Square. Particular emphasis on the coins and tokens produced by Soho, Heaton, Kings Norton, Birmingham and Watt Mints. Tel: 0121 235 2834.

Blackburn
Blackburn Museum, Museum Street. Major collections of classical and medieval English, British and Commonwealth coins. Tel: 01254 667130.

Bolton
Museum and Art Gallery, Civic Centre. Large general collection. Tel: 01204 22311.

Bradford
Bolling Hall Museum, Bolling Hall Road. English and British coins and tokens. Tel: 01274 723057.
Cartwright Hall Museum and Art Gallery, Lister Park. Roman coins from local hoards. Tel: 01274 493313.

Bristol
City Museum, Queen's Road. Ancient British, Roman, English hammered coins and coins of the Bristol Mint. Tel: 0117 927256.

Cambridge
Fitzwilliam Museum, Trumpington Street. Whole world from classical to modern, including English medieval and later British coins. Tel: 01223 332900.

Cardiff
National Museum & Galleries of Wales, Cathays Park. Greek, Roman, Celtic, English and British coins. Tel: 029 2039 7951.

Carlisle
Tullie House, Castle Street. Roman, medieval and later coins, including local counterfeiter's moulds. Tel: 01228 34781.

Chelmsford
Chelmsford and Essex Museum, Oaklands Park, Moulsham Street. Ancient British, Roman, medieval and later coins. Tel: 01245 353066.

Cheltenham
Art Gallery and Museum, Clarence Street. Roman, Anglo-Saxon and medieval English coins and Gloucestershire tokens. Tel: 01242 237 431.

Chester
Grosvenor Museum, Grosvenor Street. Roman, Anglo-Saxon, medieval English and later coins with emphasis on the Chester and Rhuddlan Mints, and Cheshire tokens. Tel: 01244 21616.

Christchurch
Red House Museum, Quay Road. Ancient British, Roman and medieval coins from hoards in Hampshire and Dorset. Tel: 01202 482860.

Colchester
Colchester and Essex Museum, The Castle. Ancient British, Roman, medieval and later English coins and Essex tokens. Tel: 01206 712931.

Derby
Museum and Art Gallery, The Strand. Roman and English coins and Derbyshire tokens. Tel: 01332 255586.

Doncaster
Museum and Art Gallery, Chequer Road. Roman, English and British coins and Yorkshire tokens. Tel: 01302 734293.

Dorchester
Dorset County Museum. Roman, medieval English and British coins. Tel: 01305 262735.

Douglas (Isle of Man)
Manx Museum. Viking, Hiberno-Norse and Manx coins and tokens. Tel: 01624 675522.

Dublin
National Museum of Ireland, Collins Barracks, Benburb Street. Vast collection covering all areas and periods but particularly strong on Irish coins. Tel: 00351 677 7444.

Dumfries
Burgh Museum. The Observatory, Corberry Hill. Classical, Anglo-Saxon medieval English and Scottish coins. Tel: 01387 53374.

Durham
The Cathedral Treasury, The College. Classical and medieval English coins, with emphasis on the ecclesiastical coinage of Durham. Tel: 0191 384 4854.

Edinburgh
Royal Museum of Scotland, Queen Street. Roman, Anglo-Saxon, Scottish and English coins, Scottish trade and communion tokens. Tel: 0131 335 7534.

Exeter
Royal Albert Memorial Museum, Queen Street. Roman and medieval English, especially coins of the Exeter Mint. Tel: 01392 265858.

Glasgow
Hunterian Museum, Glasgow University, University Avenue. A very wide range of coins of the world, with emphasis on Roman, Scottish, English and Irish coins. Tel: 0141 339 8855.

Gloucester
City Museum and Art Gallery, Brunswick Road. Ancient British, Roman, Anglo-Saxon and medieval coins from local mints. Gloucestershire tokens. Tel: 01452 524131.

Guernsey
Guernsey Museum and Art Gallery, St Peter Port. Armorican, Roman, medieval and modern Guernsey coins. Tel: 01481 726518.

Guildford
Guildford Museum, Castle Arch. Roman and medieval English coins. Tel: 01483 444750.

Hastings
Public Museum and Art Gallery, John's Place, Cambridge Road. General collection of English and British coins as well as coins from local mints. Tel: 01424 721952.

Hereford
City Museum, Broad Street. Coins of the Hereford Mint and Herefordshire tokens. Tel: 01432 268121.

Hertford
Hertford Museum, 18 Bull Plain. Ancient British, Roman, medieval and later English coins. Tel: 01992 582686.

Hull
Hull and East Riding Museum, 36 High Street. Celtic, Roman and medieval coins. Tel: 01482 593902.

Jersey
Jersey Museum, Weighbridge, St Helier. Armorican, Gallo-Belgic, Roman, medieval English and modern Jersey coins. Tel: 01534 30511.

Lancaster
City Museum, Old Town Hall, Market Square. Roman, Anglo-Saxon, medieval English coins and Lancashire tokens. Tel: 01524 64637.

Leeds
City Museum, Municipal Buildings, The Headrow. Roman, Anglo-Saxon, English medieval, Scottish, Irish and modern British coins and Yorkshire tokens. Tel: 01532 478279.

Leicester
Leicester Museum and Art Gallery, New Walk. Roman, Anglo-Saxon and medieval English coins and Leicestershire tokens.

Letchworth
Museum and Art Gallery, Broadway. Ancient British coins from Camulodunum, Roman, medieval and later English coins and Hertfordshire tokens.

Lichfield
City Library, Art Gallery and Museum, Bird Street. Roman, medieval and later English coins and Staffordshire tokens. Tel: 01543 2177.

Liverpool
Liverpool Museum, William Brown Street. Roman, medieval English and later coins and tokens. Tel: 0151 207 0001.

London
Bank of England Museum, Threadneedle Street, EC2. Gold bullion, coins and tokens as well as banknotes. Tel: 020 7601 5545.
British Museum, HSBC Coin Gallery, Great Russell Street, WC1. One of the world's largest collections covering all regions and periods. Tel: 020 7636 1555.
Cuming Museum, Walworth Road, SE17, Greek, Roman, medieval English and modern British coins and tokens. Tel: 020 7703 3324.
Gunnersbury Park Museum, Acton, W3. Ancient British, classical medieval English and British coins and London tokens. Tel: 020 8992 1612.

Ludlow
Ludlow Museum, The Assembly Rooms, Castle Square. Roman and medieval coins from local finds and Shropshire tokens. Tel: 01584 873857.

Maidstone
Museum and Art Gallery. Ancient British, Roman, Anglo-Saxon, medieval and later English coins and Kent tokens. Tel: 01622 754497.

Manchester
The Manchester Museum, the University. Greek and Roman coins, medieval and later English coins. Tel: 0161 275 2634.

Newark
Newark-on-Trent Museum, Appleton Gate. Nottinghamshire tokens and siege pieces from the Civil War. Tel: 01636 702358.

Newbury
Newbury District Museum, The Wharf. Ancient British, Roman and medieval English coins. Tel: 01635 30511.

Oxford
Heberden Coin Room, Ashmolean Museum. Vast collection of all areas and periods. Tel: 01865 27800.

Peterborough
Peterborough Museum, Priestgate. Roman, Anglo-Saxon, medieval English and British coins and Cambridgeshire tokens. Tel: 01733 340 3329.

Plymouth
City Museum and Art Gallery, Drake Circus. Ancient British and Roman coins and Devon tokens. Tel: 01752 264878.

Portsmouth
City Museum, Museum Road. Roman, medieval and later coins and Hampshire tokens. Tel: 023 808 2761.

Preston
Harris Museum and Art Gallery, Market Square. English and British coins and Lancashire tokens.

Reading
Reading Museum and Art Gallery, Blagrave Street. Ancient British, Roman and medieval English coins and Berkshire tokens.

Rochdale
Rochdale Museum, Sparrow Hill. Roman and medieval coins and Rochdale tokens. Tel: 01706 41085.

Rotherham
Municipal Museum and Art Gallery, Clifton Park. Roman, medieval English coins and modern British coins. Tel: 01709 382121.

St Albans
Verulamium Museum, St Michael's. Coins from the Roman town. Tel: 01727 819339.

Salisbury
Salisbury and South Wiltshire Museum, Cathedral Close. Ancient British, Roman, Anglo-Saxon and medieval English coins from local mints. Tel : 01722 332151.

Scarborough
Scarborough Museum, The Rotunda, Vernon Road. Roman, medieval English and Scarborough siege pieces. Tel: 01723 374839.

Sheffield
City Museum, Weston Park. Roman, English and British coins and Yorkshire tokens. Tel: 0114 2768588.

Shrewsbury
Rowley's House Museum, Barker Street. Civil War coins minted at Shrewsbury. Tel: 01743 361196.

Southampton
Museum of Archaeology, God's House Tower, Town Quay. Ancient British, Roman and medieval English coins. Tel: 023 8022 0007.

Stroud
Stroud Museum, Lansdown. Ancient British, Roman, Anglo-Saxon and medieval English coins and Gloucestershire tokens. Tel: 01453 376394.

Sunderland
Museum and Art Gallery, Borough Road. Roman, medieval English and British coins, especially ecclesiastical coins of Durham. Tel: 0191 514 1235.

Tamworth
Tamworth Castle and Museum, The Holloway. Anglo-Saxon, medieval English and later coins and Staffordshire tokens. Tel: 01827 63563.

Taunton
Somerset County Museum, Taunton Castle. Celtic, Roman, Anglo-Saxon and medieval Eglish coins and Somerset tokens. Tel: 01823 255510.

Truro
Royal Cornwall Museum, River Street. English coins of all periods and Cornish tokens. Tel: 01872 72205.

Wakefield
Wakefield Museum, Wood Street. Roman and medieval coins. Tel: 01924 295351.

Waltham Abbey
Epping Forest District Museum, 39 Sun Street. Ancient British, Roman and medieval coins and Essex tokens.

Worcester
Worcester City Museum, Foregate Street. Roman, medieval and coins of the Worcester Mint. Tel: 01905 25371.

Winchester
City Museum, The Square. Roman and medieval coins and Hampshire tokens. Tel: 01962 848269.

Yeovil
Museum of South Somerset, Hendford. Roman, medieval English and later British coins and Somerset tokens. Tel: 01935 24774.

York
Castle Museum. English and British coins. Tel: 01904 653611.
Jorvik Viking Centre, Coppergate. Viking coins. Tel: 01904 643211.
Yorkshire Museum. Roman, medieval English and later British coins. Tel: 01904 629745.

Stanley Gibbons

Now Stocks a Massive Range of Lighthouse Coin and Banknote Albums and Accessories!

Numis Coin and banknote accessories

Albums and binders

Cases and boxes

Album sheets

Presentation boxes

Capsules

UV currency lamps

Coin tongs

We now offer visitors to the world's largest stamps shop at 399 Strand a fantastic range of Lighthouse coin and banknote accessories PLUS a great selection of books and catalogues from major numismatic publishers. We look forward to welcoming you or call us for a free product brochure.

Stanley Gibbons Limited, 399 Strand, London WC2R 0LX
Telephone 0207 836 8444 Fax 0207 836 7342 Email shop@stanleygibbons.co.uk
Opening Hours Monday to Friday 9am- 5:30pm Saturday 9:30am- 5:30pm

STANLEY GIBBONS
Investment Department

The market in British coins is strong, with the average very fine condition coin increasing by 15% in 2003 backed by a solid collector base. As you can see from the examples highlighted below, there have been a number of coins recording phenomenal increases in value.

Charles 1	1997	2004	% Growth
1642 Triple Unite	£5250	£8500	61.90%

Condition is paramount with coins and we are proud to be able to offer only the best quality, investment grade items. Coins are portable tangible assets that are small, easy to store and have a worldwide market. Rare gold coins also have an underlying intrinsic value and are never worth less than their weight in gold.

George III	1997	2004	% Growth
1813 Military Guinea	£800	£1750	118.75%

Mary	1997	2004	% Growth
Fine Sovereign	£4500	£7250	61.11%

The Stanley Gibbons Investment Department is forging a reputation for expert guidance and supplying portfolios that record excellent growth in value. If you would like to find out more about our alternative investment options please do not hesitate to contact a member of our Investment Department on **+ 44 (0)20 7557 4454**. Please contact us for an informal discussion, investment advice or simply to learn more about the services we offer. We also have **sample portfolios** available to highlight the quality that we can supply.

www.stanleygibbons.com/investment

CELTIC COINS

The earliest coins used in Britain were those brought over from Gaul (modern France) in the second century BC by Celtic tribes migrating from north-western Europe to Britain. The Gallo-Belgic coins were made of gold, while the Armorican coins (Channel Islands and Normandy) were of billon (low grade silver). These coins were based on staters of Philip of Macedon with the head of Apollo (obverse) and a horse (reverse). They bore no inscriptions and were progressively more blundered in design. By 95 BC similar coins were being produced in southern Britain, and classified by the places where they have mainly been found. By 35 BC coins were beginning to appear with the names of identifiable rulers of Celtic tribes in southern Britain. These coins continued to circulate after the Roman invasion but were suppressed about AD 62.

Uninscribed Issues

125–50 BC. Gallo-Belgic Gold Staters (Ambiani)

Obv: Head of Apollo. Rev: Horse.

	F	VF	EF
Type A good design	£400	£1200	£4500
Type B defaced obverse	£300	£700	£2800
Type C disintegrated	£250	£350	£2000
Type E blank obverse	£150	£300	£450
Type F (Suessiones) abstract designs			
	£280	£700	£2800
Type X VE monogram	£300	£800	£3000

Gallo-Belgic Quarter Staters (Ambiani)

Type A good design	£220	£600	£2500
Type B defaced obverse	£185	£500	£2350
Type D geometric style	£90	£175	£500
Type X VE monogram	£170	£400	£2000

95 BC–AD 10. Uninscribed Gold Staters Struck in Britain

Obv: Apollo. Rev: Horse. Very blundered designs.

Westerham (95–65 BC)	£190	£450	£2200
Chute (85–55 BC)	£150	£300	£1000
Yarmouth (80–70 BC)	£400	£650	£2500
Cheriton (80–70 BC)	£220	£450	£1000
Clacton (90–70 BC)	£300	£800	£3000
Corieltauvi (various, from)			
	£160	£350	£800
Norfolk 'wolf' type	£150	£350	£800
Whaddon Chase	£230	£450	£900
Wonersh	£350	£500	£1000
Weald	£400	£650	£1200
Iceni (various, from)	£280	£500	£900
Remic	£225	£400	£750
Dobunni	£250	£500	£850

Quarter Staters

Clacton	£150	£250	£350
North Thames	£160	£260	£400
North Kent	£150	£230	£400
Iceni	£140	£220	£320
Sussex	£100	£150	£275
Dobunni	£140	£230	£400

Silver Coins

North Thames	£75	£130	£275
South Thames	£75	£130	£275
Durotriges stater	£50	£130	£250
Durotriges half stater	£35	£100	£140
Dobunni	£35	£80	£160
Corieltauvi	£35	£90	£180
Iceni (wreath)	£25	£60	£120
Iceni (face)	£45	£90	£200

Billon (debased silver) Coins

Armorican stater	£75	£140	£375
Armorican quarter stater	£50	£120	£300

Potin Coins

Thurrock types	£30	£50	£90

Bronze Coins

Durotriges stater	£20	£40	£80
Durotriges cast bronze	£50	£100	£180
North Thames	£30	£80	£350
North Kent	£60	£120	£400

Inscribed Celtic Coins struck in Britain

Atrebates & Regni (*Berks, Hants, Surrey and Sussex*)

Commios (c.32–20 BC)

Gold stater	£500	£1000	£2500

Tincomarus (20 BC–AD 5)

Silver minim	£150	£250	£500
Silver unit	£60	£130	£260
Gold quarter stater	£130	£235	£400

Gold stater	£400	£800	£1750

Eppillus (AD 5–10)

Bronze	£500	—	—
Silver unit	£60	£130	£280
Gold quarter stater	£140	£200	£400

Verica (AD 10–40)

Silver unit	£50	£80	£200
Gold quarter stater	£150	£250	£400

Gold stater	£240	£500	£900

Epatticus (AD 25–35)

Silver minim	£50	£100	£250
Silver unit	£45	£90	£240
Gold stater	£900	£1800	£3750

Caratacus (AD 35–40)

Silver minim	£100	£200	£300
Silver unit	£150	£300	£450

Cantii (*Kent*)

Dubnovellaunos (c.15–1 BC)

Bronze unit	£50	£140	£350

Silver unit	£120	£200	£450
Gold stater	£250	£550	£850

Vosenos (AD 1–5)

Bronze unit	£90	£200	£500
Silver unit	£125	£270	£600
Gold quarter stater	£250	£540	£1000
Gold stater	£1000	£2350	£4300

Eppillus (AD 10–25)

Bronze unit	£50	£120	£420
Silver unit	£60	£130	£320
Gold quarter stater	£130	£250	£475
Gold stater	£900	£1800	£4000

Amminus (AD 15)

Bronze unit	£75	£300	£600
Silver minim	£100	£200	£400

Silver unit	£150	£300	£600

Catuvellauni (*North Thames, Beds and Herts*)

Tasciovanos (20 BC–AD 10)

Bronze half unit	£50	£120	£250

Bronze unit	£50	£120	£300
Silver unit	£75	£150	£350
Gold quarter stater	£120	£210	£435

Gold stater	£200	£400	£950

Andoco (AD 5–15)

Bronze unit	£75	£200	£340

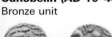

Silver unit	£145	£380	£700
Gold quarter stater	£200	£400	£750
Gold stater	£500	£1100	£2600

Cunobelin (AD 10–40)

Bronze unit	£60	£135	£300

Silver unit	£75	£150	£325
Quarter stater	£135	£250	£400
Stater	£200	£450	£950

Corieltauvi (*East Midlands, Lincs, Yorks*)

Aun Cost

Silver half unit	£75	£150	£280
Silver unit	£80	£175	£300
Stater	£250	£600	£950

Esup Asu

Silver unit	£150	£300	£500
Stater	£300	£650	£1200

Vep Corf

Silver half unit	£85	£200	£425

Silver unit	£70	£160	£275
Stater	£320	£650	£2000

Dumnoc Tigir Seno

Silver unit	£90	£175	£480
Stater	£730	£1750	£3000

Volisios Dumnocoveros

Silver half unit	£85	£175	£425
Silver unit	£90	£175	£450
Stater	£300	£700	£1500

Volisios Dumnovellaunos

Silver half unit	£135	£320	£650
Stater	£280	£650	£1200

Volisios Cartivellaunos

Silver half unit	£280	£600	£1100
Stater	£900	£1800	£3750

Iat Iso

Silver unit	£150	£400	£1100

Dobunni (*Glos. Here., Mon., Som., Wilts and Worcs*)

Anted

Silver unit	£50	£100	£280
Stater	£300	£500	£1100

Eisu

Silver unit	£50	£120	£300
Stater	£400	£700	£1450

Catti

Stater	£250	£500	£950

Cornux

Stater	£750	£1500	£3000

Corio

Quarter stater	£180	£320	£600
Stater	£250	£500	£950

Durotriges (*West Hants, Dorset, Somerset and Wilts*)

Crab

Silver minim	£90	£230	£380

Silver unit	£150	£300	£600

Iceni (*Cambs, Norfolk and Suffolk*)

Duro

Silver unit	£100	£250	£500

Anted

Silver half unit	£40	£85	£150
Silver unit	£30	£60	£180

Stater	£400	£900	£2350
Ecen			
Silver half unit	£40	£80	£175
Silver unit	£30	£60	£175
Saenu			
Silver unit	£50	£100	£275
Aesu			

Silver unit	£50	£100	£275
Prasutagus			
Silver unit	£400	£900	£1750
Ale Scala			
Silver unit	£340	£750	£1500

Trinovantes (*Essex, Middlesex, Bucks and Beds*)

Addedomaros (15–1 BC)

Gold quarter stater	£150	£300	£500
Gold stater	£250	£500	£750

Dubnovellaunos (AD 1–10)

Bronze unit	£50	£120	£400
Gold quarter stater	£150	£300	£500
Gold stater	£250	£435	£725

ROMAN BRITAIN

From about AD 43 till the middle of the 5th century Roman coins were in use in Britain and during that long period only the republican coinage produced at Rome was in use. There were no local mints for the production of subsidiary coinage (as in the eastern Roman Empire), but in the late 3rd century Carausius, commander of the Roman Channel fleet, seized power in Britain and northern Gaul (France) and opened mints at Londinium (London) and either Clausentum (near Southampton) or Camulodunum (Colchester) where distinctive coins were struck between 287 and 293. After the rebellion was suppressed London became an official branch mint and produced a number of bronze folles or billon (low-grade silver) coins, usually termed 'third brass' (Ae 3) by numismatists, until it closed down in 325. Unofficial copies and outright counterfeits of Roman coins were also produced in Britain, mainly around 270 and in the early 5th century as the Empire disintegrated. We restrict the listing of Roman coins to those struck under Carausius and Allectus (who murdered him and briefly succeeded him) or at London in the early 4th century in the names of various emperors and their relatives. Coins under Carausius and Allectus consisted of the bronze antoninianus or quinarius, the silver denarius and the gold aureus.

Carausius (287–93)

London

Antoninianus, various types from			
	£25	£50	£230
Denarius	£250	£750	£1800
Aureus	£8000	£18,000	—

Colchester or Clausentum

Antoninianus, various types from			
	£75	£150	£600
Denarius	£400	£1000	—

Allectus (293–6)

London

Antoninianus, various types from			
	£25	£60	£280
Quinarius	£25	£60	£240
Aureus	£8000	£24,000	—

Clausentum or Colchester

Quinarius	£40	£80	£175
Antoninianus, various types from			
	£40	£100	£300

London under Imperial Control (296–325)

Constantius (293–306)

Follis	£12	£30	£100

Galerius (305–11)

Follis	£10	£30	£85

Severus II (306–7)

Follis	£35	£85	£250

Maximinus II (309–13)

Follis	£12	£30	£100

Maxentius (306–12)

Follis	£6	£20	£50
Licinius I (308–24)			
Follis	£5	£15	£45
Licinius II (317–24)			
Ae 3	£8	£20	£50
Constantine I (307–37)			
Follis	£8	£20	£60
Ae 3	£8	£20	£60
Fausta (wife of Constantine)			
Ae 3	£50	£135	£350
Helena (mother of Constantine)			
Ae 3	£50	£135	£350
Crispus Caesar (317–26)			
Ae 3	£10	£20	£50
Constantine II			
Ae 3	£12	£25	£70

ANGLO-SAXON COINAGE

The period between the withdrawal of the Roman legions about 407 and the arrival of St Augustine in Kent in 597 is regarded as the Dark Ages, characterised by the breakdown of law and order, the decay of towns and cities and the increasing incursions of Angles, Saxons and Jutes who came at first to pillage but later to form permanent settlements. These Teutonic marauders seem to have relied on the gold tremisses (third-solidus) produced by the Merovingian Franks, successors to the Roman Empire in what is now France. From these coins were derived the Anglo-Saxon thrymsas of the early 7th century. The Frankish deniers (derived from the Roman denarius) gave rise to the silver sceats or sceattas, the ancestor of the silver penny which gradually replaced the sceat as it was increasingly debased. There are many different types of these coins, produced in the seven kingdoms which were gradually unified in the 10th century, and we only list a representative range. Coins in this section are priced in three grades: F (Fine), VF (Very Fine) and EF (Extremely Fine). Coins are silver pennies, unless otherwise stated.

Early Period (600–750)

Copper styca, various types from			
	£20	£50	£120
Silver sceat, various types from			
	£50	£120	£400

Northumbria (685–867)

Aldfrith (685–705)

Sceat	£500	£1200	—

Eadberht (737–58)

Sceat	£175	£400	£1000

Alcred (765–74)

Sceat	£350	£900	£2000

Aethelred I (774–9 and 789–96)

Sceat, several types from	£180	£400	£1000

Eanred (810–54)

Copper styca	£50	£100	£300

Aethelred II (854–62)

Sceat	£25	£40	£100

Osbehrt (862–7)

Sceat	£75	£160	£400

Archbishops of York

Ecgberht (c.732–66)

Sceat, several types from	£70	£150	£380

Wigmund (837–54)

Copper styca	£20	£50	£150

Wulfhere (854–900)

Penny	£100	£250	£500

Anglo-Saxon Middle Period (780–973)

In this period three kingdoms emerged as the dominant political entities, in Kent, Mercia (the Midlands) and Wessex, and it was out of the latter that all England was eventually unified. In the same period, however, Viking raids led to permanent settlement in what came to be known as the Danelaw (north-eastern counties but gradually encroaching on the south and west). Despite political differences, these kingdoms generally had their silver pennies struck at Canterbury. Offa of Mercia is credited with the first penny, struck in sterling silver and widely imitated thereafter. For more than five centuries it was virtually the only English coin and continued without major alterations until Tudor times.

Kent

Ecgberht (c.780)	£1750	£4000	—
Eadberht Praen (796-98)	£1750	£4000	—
Cuthred (798–807), various types from			
	£500	£1250	—
Baldred (c.823–25), various types from			
	£650	£1750	—

Archbishops of Canterbury

Jaenberht (765–92), various types from			
	£1000	£2650	—
Aethelweard (792–805), various types from			
	£800	£2000	—

Wulfred (805–32), various types from			
	£560	£2000	—
Ceolnoth (833–70), various types from			
	£400	£1000	—

Aethered (870–89), various types from			
	£1300	£3750	—
Plegmund (890–914), various types from			
	£500	£1250	—

Mercia

Offa (757–96)

Non-portrait types from	£400	£850	£2000
Portrait types from	£650	£1750	£4000
Queen Cynethryth			
Non-portrait types from	£900	£2400	£4500
Portrait types from	£1600	£5000	—

Coenwulf (796–821)

Portrait types from	£500	£750	£2000
Non-portrait types from	£400	£600	£1500
Ceolwulf I (821–23)			
Portrait types from	£700	£1500	£4000
Beornwulf (823–25)			
Portrait types from	£800	£2500	—

Ludica (825–27)

Portrait type	£2500	£7000	—
Wiglaf (827–29 and 830–40)			
Portrait type	£1750	£4500	—
Non-portrait type	£1400	£4000	—
Behrtwulf (840–52)			
Portrait types from	£650	£1500	£4000
Non-portrait types from	£750	£1850	—
Burgred (852–74)			
Portrait types from	£100	£220	£600
Ceolwulf II (874–880)			
Portrait type	£1700	£7500	—

East Anglia

Beonna (c.758)

Sceat (Roman lettering)	£350	£750	£1000
Sceat (Runic lettering)	£650	£1200	—

Eadwald (c.796–98)
Non-portrait types   £800   £1800   £4000

Aethelstan I (c.825–40)

Portrait types from   £800   £2000   £5000
Non-portrait types from   £600   £1300   £4000

Aethelweard (c.840–55)
Non-portrait types from   £400   £900   £2000

Eadmund (855–70)
Non-portrait types from   £180   £400   £950

Danish East Anglia

Guthrum (Aethelstan II) (878–90)
             £1200   £3000   —
St Edmund memorial penny
             £100   £200   £500
St Edmund halfpenny   £450   £900   £2000
St Martin of Lincoln (c.925)
             £1600   £4500   —

Danelaw (c.898–915)

Alfred (Viking imitation), various from
             £300   £650   £1800
Plegmund (Danish imitation)
             £350   £800   £2000

Viking York

Siefred or Sievert (c.897)
Small cross types from   £100   £180   £600
Cross on steps   £300   £750   £1500

Cnut
Various pennies from   £100   £200   £750
Halfpenny   £400   £700   £1800
St Peter penny   £175   £450   £800
St Peter halfpenny   £600   £1000   £3000
Regnald I (c.919–21)   £1350   £3500   —
Sihtric I (921–27)   £1500   £4000   —
Anlaf Guthfrithsson
(939–54)   £1300   £3600   —
Olaf Guthfrithsson   £2500   £6000   —

Olaf Sihtricsson (941–44, 948–52)
Various types from   £1300   £3500   —
Regnald II (943–44)   £2500   £8000   —
Sihtric II (942–3)   £1800   £4000   —

Eric Blood-axe (948, 952–54)
Cross/moneyer type   £2000   £7000   —

Sword/cross type   £2300   £6500   —

Wessex

Beorhtric (782–802)   10,000   —   —

Ecgberht (802–39)
Portrait types from   £1000   £2000   £5000
Non-portrait types from   £750   £1500   £4000

Aethelwulf (839–58)
Canterbury   £250   £500   £2000
Rochester   £400   £750   £2500

Aethelberht (858–66)
Cross reverse   £300   £500   £900

Cross fleury over quatrefoil
             £800   £1750   £3000

Aethelred I (866–71)
Moneyer's name in one line
             £300   £750   £1600
Moneyer's name in four lines
             £650   £1600   £3000

Alfred the Great (871–99)
Portrait, AELBRED type   £300   £600   £1750
London reverse   £750   £1500   £3000
London halfpenny   £400   £750   £2000
Non-portrait types from   £350   £700   £1800
Non-portrait halfpennies from
             £450   £750   £2000

Edward the Elder (899–924)

Non-portrait types from	£150	£300	£750
Non-portrait halfpennies	£700	£1500	£3250
Portrait types from	£400	£1000	£2500

Floral types from	£850	£2400	£5000
Hand of God	£1600	£4000	—
Architectural types from	£1000	£2400	£6000

Aethelstan (924–39)

Non-portrait types from	£175	£400	£900
Cross / cross types	£220	£500	£900
Portrait types / moneyer's name in two lines			
	£600	£1500	£3000
Portrait types / small cross reverse			
	£400	£750	£1600
Floral types (North Mercia) from			
	£300	£600	£1800
Small cross / tower types (North East)			
	£800	£1750	£4000
Bust in high relief	£550	£1250	£2500
Helmeted bust	£650	£1500	£4000

Eadmund (939–46)

Non-portrait types from	£180	£400	£1000

Non-portrait halfpennies	£650	£1400	£3000
Crowned bust	£450	£900	£2000
Helmeted bust	£750	£1600	£3000

Eadred (946–55)

Non-portrait types (cross)	£170	£360	£750
Non-portrait types (rosette)			
	£200	£450	£900
Halfpennies	£500	£1000	£2300

Eadwig (955–59)

Cross / moneyer's name in two lines			
	£200	£400	£900
Cross / moneyer's name in one line			
	£700	£2300	£5000
Rosette or small cross on reverse			
	£280	£600	£2000
Portrait / small cross	£2000	£7000	—

Kings of All England

Eadgar (957–75)

Eadgar was King of Mercia and Northumbria from 957 and King of All England from 959 till 975. The coinage was reformed in 973, when a bust became the standard obverse type, with a cross on the reverse and the inscription round the circle.

Non-portrait types from	£120	£250	£750

Cross / cross types from	£110	£240	£700
Rosette / rosette types from			
	£150	£380	£1000
Halfpennies	£800	£2000	£4000
Portrait types, pre-reform	£550	£1300	£3500
Portrait halfpennies	£650	£1350	£4000
Reform: bust obverse, small cross reverse			
	£650	£1400	£5000

Edward the Martyr (975–78)

Penny	£650	£1450	£6000

Aethelred II 'the Unready' (978–1016)

Small cross	£350	£750	£2000
Large hand	£100	£160	£300
Small hand	£90	£150	£275
Benediction hand	£500	£1000	£2300
CRUX in angles of cross	£75	£150	£400
Long cross	£80	£135	£280
Helmeted bust	£90	£200	£450

Lamb of God / Dove	£3300	—	—

Cnut (1016–35)

Quatrefoil	£70	£135	£350
Helmet	£85	£140	£400
Short cross	£80	£140	£400
Jewelled cross	£600	£1200	£2000

Harold I (1035–40)

Jewelled cross	200	£400	£1000
Long cross and trefoils	£185	£375	£600
Long cross and fleur de lis			
	£175	£350	£500

Harthacnut (1035–42)

Jewelled cross, bust left	£800	£2000	£5000

Bust right	£700	£1800	£4500

Arm and sceptre type with name Harthacnut

	£650	£1500	£3000
As above but name Cnut	£450	£1200	£2500
Lund copies	£200	£500	£780

Edward the Confessor (1042–66)

PACX type	£150	£450	£900
Radiate crown	£80	£150	£400
Trefoil quadrilateral	£80	£140	£380
Short cross, small flan	£75	£130	£350

Expanding cross, light or heavy issues

	£75	£140	£400
Helmet types	£80	£140	£400
Sovereign / eagles	£100	£210	£450
Hammer cross	£80	£140	£400

Facing bust	£80	£160	£400
Pyramids or piles	£85	£180	£500

Large facing bust with sceptre

	£950	£2500	£5000

Harold II (1066)

Crowned bust left with sceptre / PAX

	£450	£900	£1800

As above, but no sceptre	£500	£1000	£3000
Bust right with sceptre	£750	£2000	—

Norman Kings (1066–1154)

The Normans were content with the existing English system of coinage and continued to strike silver pennies of good quality. In the reign of William the Conqueror production was devolved to about 70 boroughs whose names appear in various forms on the reverse, but the number of mints was progressively reduced in later reigns and by the time of Henry III production was confined to the mints in London and Canterbury as well as the coins struck at the Episcopal mints in York and Canterbury. In this period the prominent cross on the reverse facilitated the cutting of pennies into halves and fourths (farthings) and as a result coins of these denominations were very seldom minted.

William I (1066–87)

Left profile / cross fleury	£200	£450	£1000

Full face, bonnet type	£140	£300	£900
Canopy type	£250	£450	£1000
Two sceptres	£180	£400	£900
Two stars	£135	£300	£850
Sword	£200	£450	£1000
Right profile	£300	£700	£2000
PAXS type	£120	£230	£850

William II (1087–1100)

Halfpennies	£1500	£2750	—
Right profile	£375	£800	£2200

Cross in quatrefoil	£350	£750	£1800
Cross voided	£350	£700	£1800
Cross pattee and fleury	£400	£800	£2000
Cross fleury and piles	£450	£1000	£3000

Henry I (1100–35)

Annulets	£350	£750	£2000
Left profile / cross fleury	£200	£500	£900
PAX	£210	£450	£800

Facing bust / annulets and piles

	£275	£700	£1800

Voided cross with fleurs in angles

	£500	£1100	£3000
Pointing bust and stars	£750	£1750	£4000

Facing bust / quatrefoils and piles

	£240	£550	£1000

Large bust / cross with annulets in angles

	£900	£1900	£5000

Facing bust / cross in quatrefoil

£475	£1000	£2500

Small facing bust in circle / cross fleury

£140	£320	£800

Very large bust / double inscription

£450	£900	£1800

Small bust / cross with annulets in angles

£280	£650	£1000
Star in lozenge fleury	£280	£650	£1000
Pellets in quatrefoil	£160	£400	£950
Quatrefoil on cross fleury	£110	£280	£650

Stephen (1135–54)

Cross Moline (Watford)	£150	£350	£800
PERERIC	£400	£900	£2000

Facing bust / voided cross and mullets

£160	£400	£1100

Left profile with sceptre / cross fleury

£300	£650	£1800

Half-left bust / voided cross pommee

£130	£400	£1000

Civil War

Coins struck from defaced dies

many types from	£400	£1000	—

Henry, Earl of Northumberland

	£1500	£4000	—
Flag type (York)	£1500	£3500	—

Stephen and Matilda (1153)

	£2750	£6000	—
Eustace (Stephen's son)	£2500	£5500	—
Empress Matilda	£1000	£3500	—
Duke Henry (Matilda's son)			
	£2500	£6000	—
William of Gloucester	£2800	£6500	—

Plantagenet Kings (1154–1399)

Following the prolonged civil wars between the followers of Stephen and Matilda the coinage was in a very poor shape. In 1158 Henry II (Matilda's son) reformed the coinage and instituted a new type, known as the Cross-and-crosslet type from the reverse motif, sometimes known as the Tealby coinage, from a large hoard found there in 1807. Some 30 mints took part in the recoinage but only 11 continued to operate after this work was completed. The quality of this coinage was well below the usual standards and for this reason coins are exceptionally priced here in Fair, F and VF grades. The coinage was again reformed in 1180 when the so-called Short Cross type was introduced. Thereafter coins are priced in F, VF and EF states. Henry III again changed the style by extending the arms of the cross to the rim to prevent clipping. The Long Cross type, introduced in 1247, continued till the end of the Middle Ages. The first coin of a larger value than a penny was the groat (fourpence), introduced in 1279, while the first regular gold coinage was not issued until 1344. At the other extreme, silver halfpennies and farthings were seldom produced before 1279.

Henry II (1154–89)

Cross and crosslet, six bust variants

£30	£70	£180

Short cross, three types from

£40	£90	£250

Richard I (1189–99)

Short cross, various types from

£30	£110	£280

John (1199–1216)

Short cross, as above but neater

£35	£80	£140

Henry III (1216–72)

Short cross, various types from

£18	£35	£110

Long Cross without sceptre £18 £35 £90

Long cross with sceptre £20 £40 £100

Edward I (1272–1307)

Long Cross with sceptre, very crude

	£25	£60	£120

New coinage (1279)

Farthing	£12	£30	£120
Halfpenny	£20	£50	£135
Penny	£15	£30	£70
Groat	£1000	£3600	——

Edward II (1307–27)

Farthing	£30	£70	£130
Halfpenny	£50	£120	£300

Penny	£20	£45	£100

Edward III (1327–77)

First coinage (1327–35) .925 fine

Farthing, London or Berwick, from

£40	£75	£200

Halfpenny, London or Berwick, from

£50	£130	£600

Penny, various mints from

£225	£500	£1200

Second coinage (1335–43) .833 fine

Farthing, London, various from

	£40	£120	£500
Halfpenny, London	£20	£40	£120
Halfpenny, Reading	£350	£600	£1200

Third coinage (1344–51) .925, bushy hair

Farthing	£40	£90	£235
Halfpenny, London	£12	£35	£100
Halfpenny, Reading	£300	£600	——
Penny, London	£12	£30	£100
Penny, Canterbury	£50	£120	£250

Penny, Durham, various from

£50	£100	£250

Penny, Reading	£230	£460	£1000
Penny, York	£30	£80	£250

Helm or quarter-florin (1s 6d)

——	——	——

Leopard or half-florin (3s)	——	——	——
Leopard (6s)	——	——	——

Quarter noble (1s 8d), various from

£400	£800	£1800

Half noble (3s 4d)	£1250	£3250	£7000

Noble (6s 8d), various from

£900	£2000	£3500

Pre-treaty coinage (1351–61) with French title

Farthing, various from	£150	£325	£1000
Halfpenny, various from	£100	£275	£600

Penny, London, various from

£20	£60	£200

Penny, Durham, various from

£25	£70	£300

Penny, York royal mint	£30	£60	£140

York, Archbishop Thoresby, various from

£20	£40	£120

Half groat, London, various from

£22	£60	£180

Half groat, York, various from

£40	£90	£400

Groat, London, various from

£35	£100	£280

Quarter noble, various from	£160	£350	£650
Half noble, various from	£275	£600	£1200
Noble, various from	£75	£800	£1500

Transitional Treaty period (1361) Lord of Aquitaine, or no French title at all

Halfpenny	£80	£200	£900
Penny, London	£80	£220	£1000
Penny, Durham	£70	£180	£900
Penny, York, Archbishop Thoresby	£60	£140	£600
Half groat	£90	£220	£1000
Groat	£140	£500	£1500
Quarter noble, various from	£160	£300	£2000
Half noble	£180	£425	£2500

Noble	£350	£650	£3000

Treaty period (1361–69) French title omitted. New style of lettering.

Farthing	£80	£240	£1000
Halfpenny	£30	£60	£130
Penny, London, various from	£25	£50	£120
Penny, Calais	£80	£200	£900
Penny, Durham, various from	£50	£120	£400
Penny, York, five types from	£25	£60	£120
Half groat, London, various from	£25	£60	£140
Half groat, Calais	£110	£230	£800

Groat, London, various from	£50	£110	£600
Groat, Calais	£120	£280	£850
Quarter noble, London, various from	£120	£220	£750
Quarter noble, Calais, various from	£130	£240	£900
Half noble, London, various from	£160	£320	£1200
Half noble, Calais, flag at stern	£240	£600	£1500
Half noble, Calais, no flag	£275	£700	£1800
Noble, London, various from	£260	£530	£1400
Noble, Calais, flag at stern	£300	£600	£2400
Noble, Calais, no flag	£300	£650	£2500

Post Treaty period (1369–77) French title restored.

Farthing	£170	£350	£1400
Penny, London, various from	£40	£100	£220
Penny, Durham, various from	£50	£120	£260
Penny, York, various from	£25	£70	£200
Half groat, various from	£100	£260	£600

Groat, various from	£80	£200	£500
Half noble, London	£750	£1600	£3000
Half noble, Calais, various from	£360	£800	£2000
Noble, London, various from	£300	£550	£1350
Noble, Calais, various from	£275	£500	£1200

Richard II (1377–99)

Farthing, various from	£100	£375	£1000
Halfpenny, various from	£25	£75	£200
Penny, London, various from	£160	£450	£1400
Penny, Durham	£180	£500	£1500
Penny, York. Many types from	£30	£120	£250

Half groat, various from	£175	£500	£1400
Groat, various from	£200	£600	£1600
Quarter noble, various from			
	£200	£350	£900
Half noble, London, various from			
	£450	£1000	£3000
Half noble, Calais, various from			
	£550	£1500	£3500
Noble, London, various from			
	£500	£900	£2000

| Noble, Calais, various from | | | |
| | £475 | £1000 | £2500 |

Lancastrian Kings (1399–1471)

Henry IV (1399–1413)

Heavy coinage (1399–1412)

Farthing	£550	£1000	£2500
Halfpenny	£150	£300	£900
Penny, London	£550	£1400	£2500
Penny, York	£240	£650	£1200
Half groat	£1100	£2750	£4000

Quarter noble, London, two types from			
	£750	£1700	£3500
Quarter noble, Calais	£900	£2000	£4000
Half noble, London	£4000	—	—
Half noble, Calais	£6000	—	—
Noble, London	£2750	£6000	—
Noble, Calais	£3250	£7500	—

Light coinage (1412–13)

Farthing	£480	£1000	£2000
Halfpenny	£150	£350	£1000
Penny, London, various from			
	£425	£950	£2000

Penny, Durham	£180	£600	£1500
Penny, York	£180	£600	£1500
Half groat, various from	£550	£1200	£2400
Groat, various from	£1250	£3000	£7500
Half noble	£2750	—	—
Noble	£800	£1750	£4000

Henry V (1413–22)

| Farthing | £150 | £350 | £1000 |

Halfpenny, various from	£22	£60	£200
Penny, London, six types, from			
	£30	£60	£200
Penny, Durham, three types from			
	£60	£150	£600
Penny, York, seven types from			
	£22	£75	£230

Half groat, eight types from			
	£75	£220	£700
Groat, 10 types from	£75	£200	£500
Quarter noble, five types from			
	£160	£400	£1000
Half noble, six types from			
	£325	£700	£1500
Noble, nine types from	£350	£700	£1500

Henry VI (First reign 1422–61)

The coinage of this reign is distinguished by the use of various symbols, in addition to the mint-marks which fix the chronology of each issue, and they are grouped accordingly. Royal mints were reactivated at Calais (1424–40) and York (1423–4).

Annulet issue (1422–27)

Farthing, London	£160	£275	£900
Farthing, Calais	£230	£475	£1000
Halfpenny, London	£18	£45	£100
Halfpenny, Calais	£18	£45	£120
Halfpenny, York	£375	£800	£1600
Penny, London	£30	£70	£200
Penny, Calais	£25	£60	£175
Penny, York	£550	£750	£2200
Half groat, London	£30	£60	£200
Half groat, Calais, two types from			
	£30	£55	£180
Half groat, York	£700	£1600	£4000
Groat, London	£35	£80	£175
Groat, Calais, two types from			
	£30	£60	£120
Groat, York	£675	£1500	£3850
Quarter noble, London, three types from			
	£135	£240	£800
Quarter noble, Calais, three types from			
	£175	£375	£900
Quarter noble, York	£240	£430	£950
Half noble, London, two types from			
	£225	£375	£900
Half noble, Calais, two types from			
	£350	£700	£2000
Half noble, York	£375	£800	£2400

Noble, London, three types from			
	£240	£450	£1100
Noble, Calais, two types from			
	£400	£700	£2000
Noble, York	£425	£760	£2400

Annulet-Trefoil issue (1427)

Penny, Calais, two types from			
	£60	£160	£750
Half groat, Calais	£50	£135	£700
Groat, Calais	£50	£145	£725

Rosette-Mascle issue (1427–30)

Farthing, London	£120	£240	£800
Farthing, Calais	£140	£350	£1000
Halfpenny, London	£25	£60	£120
Halfpenny, Calais	£25	£60	£130
Penny, London	£70	£135	£700
Penny, Calais	£35	£75	£200

Penny, York, three types from			
	£30	£70	£150
Half groat, London	£50	£120	£450
Half groat, Calais	£30	£60	£140
Groat, London	£50	£90	£260
Groat, Calais, two types from			
	£40	£75	£150
Quarter noble, London, two types from			
	£260	£550	£850

Quarter noble, Calais   £375   £600 £1750

Quarter noble, Calais	£375	£600	£1750
Half noble, London	£300	£600	£1200
Half noble, Calais	£850	£1750	£4000
Noble, London	£540	£1200	£3500
Noble, Calais	£575	£1300	£4000

Pinecone-Mascle issue (1430–34)

Farthing, London	£135	£300	£1000
Farthing, Calais	£200	£460	£1300
Halfpenny, London	£25	£50	£120
Halfpenny, Calais	£25	£60	£150
Penny, London	£60	£110	£200
Penny, Calais	£35	£80	£250
Penny, Durham	£45	£95	£300
Penny, York, three types from			
	£30	£70	£230
Half groat, London	£45	£100	£300
Half groat, Calais	£30	£60	£150
Groat, London	£40	£75	£180
Groat, London	£35	£70	£160
Quarter noble	—	—	—
Half noble	—	—	—
Noble	£550	£1200	£2500

Leaf-Mascle issue (1434–5)

Halfpenny, London	£30	£70	£200
Halfpenny, Calais	£60	£125	£260
Penny, London	£45	£110	£200
Penny, Calais	£45	£110	£220
Half groat, London	£45	£110	£220
Half groat, Calais	£40	£100	£200
Groat, London, two types from			
	£60	£120	£220
Groat, Calais	£40	£110	£200

Quarter noble	£800	£1600	£4000
Half noble	—	—	—
Noble	£1600	£3250	£5000

Leaf-Trefoil issue (1435–8)

Farthing, London	£120	£350	£1000
Halfpenny, London, two types from			
	£30	£60	£120
Penny, London	£55	£110	£230
Penny, Calais	£220	£540	£900
Penny, Durham	£90	£240	£750
Half groat, London, three types from			
	£40	£90	£250

Groat, London, two types from			
	£40	£90	£250
Groat, Calais	£425	£800	£2300
Noble	£2250	£5000	£8000

Trefoil issue (1438–43)

Halfpenny, London	£35	£80	£250
Half groat, London	£230	£450	£1000
Half groat, Calais	—	—	—

Groat, London, three types from			
	£45	£120	£250
Groat, Calais	£120	£375	£800
Noble	£1600	£3750	£6000

Trefoil-Pellet issue (1443–45)

Groat	£50	£150	£350

Leaf-Pellet issue (1445–54)

Farthing	£160	£350	£750
Halfpenny, two types from			
	£22	£55	£100
Penny, London, three types from			
	£40	£90	£200
Penny, Durham, two types from			
	£85	£210	£400
Penny, York, two types from			
	£30	£75	£250
Half groat, London, two types from			
	£40	£100	£250
Groat, London, five types from			
	£35	£85	£230
Noble	£1600	£3750	£7000

Unmarked issue (1453–4)

Half groat	£180	£450	£1000
Groat, two types from	£225	£550	£1250

Cross-Pellet issue (1454–60)

Farthing	£160	£350	£800
Halfpenny, two types from			
	£40	£90	£300
Penny, London	£120	£300	£1000
Penny, Durham	£120	£275	£850
Penny, York	£45	£100	£300
Half groat, London	£200	£430	£1200

Groat, London, four types from			
	£75	£150	£500

Lis-Pellet issue (1456–60)

Groat, London	£175	£360	£1200

Edward IV (first reign, 1461–70)

Inflation and the rising costs of the Wars of the Roses led to a reduction in the weight of the silver coinage in 1264. As the noble was now worth 8s 4d it was necessary to introduce new gold coins, hence the ryal or rose noble (10s) and the angel (6s 8d or one third of a pound). Regal mints were opened at Canterbury and York to cope with the recoinage, while temporary mints were also briefly in operation at Bristol, Coventry and Norwich.

Heavy coinage (1461–64)

Farthing	£550	£1400	—
Halfpenny, five types from	£50	£130	£400
Penny, London, four types from			
	£175	£400	£800
Penny, Durham	£170	£375	£800
Penny, York	£140	£280	£600
Half groat, London, four types from			
	£220	£475	£900
Groat, London, nine types from			
	£60	£150	£500

Noble	£3500	£7000	—

Light coinage (1464–70)

Farthing, London, two types from			
	£450	—	—
Halfpenny, London, three types from			
	£35	£80	£250
Halfpenny, Bristol, two types from			
	£140	£300	£750
Halfpenny, Canterbury regal mint			
	£90	£140	£300
Halfpenny, Archbishop Bourchier			
	£110	£240	£600
Penny, London, six types from			
	£40	££75	£200
Penny, Bristol, three types from			
	£110	£240	£600
Penny, Canterbury regal mint			
	£140	£350	£800
Penny, Canterbury, Bourchier, 4 types from			
	£85	£160	£350
Penny, Durham, eight types from			
	£25	££80	£220
Penny, York, six types from			
	£30	£80	£250
Half groat, London, five types from			
	£50	£100	£220
Half groat, Bristol, four types from			
	£75	£210	£400
Half groat, Canterbury regal mint, 4 types			
	£25	£80	£250
Half groat, Canterbury, Bourchier, 6 types			
	£30	£60	£230
Half groat, Coventry	—	—	—
Half groat, Norwich	—	—	—
York, four types from	£60	£120	£350
Groat, London, many types from			
	£40	£80	£250
Groat, Bristol, four types from			
	£40	£75	£240
Groat, Coventry, three types			
	£50	£140	£300
Norwich	£60	£150	£600
York, three types from	£40	£80	£240

Quarter ryal (2s 6d), three types from

	£185	£425	£1000
Half ryal (5s), London	£260	£450	£1500
Half ryal, Bristol	£375	£900	£2000
Half ryal, Coventry	—	—	—
Half ryal, Norwich	£1300	£2750	£4500

Angel (6s 8d), two types — — —

Ryal (10s), London, three types from

	£325	£550	£1500
Ryal, Bristol, two types from			
	£360	£700	£2000
Ryal, Coventry	£700	£1500	£4500
Ryal, Norwich	£800	£1650	£5000

Ryal, York, two types from

	£340	£750	£2000

Henry VI (restored 1470–71)

Halfpenny, London	£160	£375	£1000
Penny, London	£350	£800	£2000
Penny, York	£225	£450	£900
Half groat, London	£250	£500	£1200
Groat, London	£110	£235	£500
Groat, Bristol	£175	£350	£600
Groat, York	£125	£260	£550
Half angel, London	£1500	£3250	£6000

Angel, London	£550	£1300	£4000
Angel, Bristol	£900	£2000	—

Edward IV (second reign 1471–83)

Halfpenny, London, two types from

	£25	£70	£200
Halfpenny, Canterbury regal mint, 3 types			
	£75	£145	£600
Halfpenny, Durham, three types from			
	£140	£275	£1000
Penny, London	£40	£90	£250
Penny, Bristol	£350	£600	—
Penny, Canterbury regal mint, two types			
	£70	£145	£300

Penny, Durham, Bishop Booth, 7 types			
	£25	£70	£200
Penny, Durham, Sede Vacante (1476)			
	£40	£120	£300
Penny, Durham, Bishop Dudley, 2 types			
	£25	£60	£180
Penny, York, Archb Neville, many types			
	£20	£60	£200
Penny, York, Sede Vacante (1476)			
	£25	£70	£250
Penny, York, Archb. Booth	£25	£60	£200
Penny, York, Sede Vacante (1480)			
	£25	£50	£200
Penny, York, Archb. Rotherham, 3 types			
	£20	£60	£180
Half groat, London	£40	£90	£250
Half groat, Canterbury, four types			
	£30	£75	£220
Half groat, York	£100	£250	£500
Groat, London, five types from			
	£35	£80	£230
Groat, Bristol	£70	£175	£400
Groat, York	£75	£180	£450
Half angel, London, three types from			
	£180	£400	£2000

Angel, London	£225	£450	£2250
Angel, Bristol	£800	£1750	£5000

Edward IV or V (1483)

Coins with the name Edward but mint mark of halved sun and rose, are believed to have been used during the 11-week reign of the 12 year-old son of Edward IV, the elder of the Princes in the Tower, murdered on the orders of their uncle who seized the throne as Richard III.

Halfpenny	£150	£450	£1000
Penny	£700	£1500	£4000
Groat	£500	£1000	£2500
Half angel	—	—	—
Angel	£1300	£3300	£7000

Richard III (1483–85)

Halfpenny, London, two types from			
	£150	£300	£600
Penny, London	—	—	—
Penny, Durham	£120	£320	£800
Penny, York, three types from			
	£140	£325	£900
Half groat, London, three types from			
	£800	£1600	£4000
Groat, London, two types from			
	£250	£475	£1500
Groat, York	£375	£900	£3000

Half angel	—	—	—
Angel, several types from			
	£800	£1600	—

Tudor Monarchy (1485–1603)

The period of the Tudor kings and queens is marked by a revolution in coin design and techniques of production. In the reign of Henry VII alone coins shed their medieval lettering and stylised portraiture and adopted Renaissance fashions in design. Henry introduced several new coins, notably the gold sovereign and the silver testoon or shilling. In the reign of Henry VIII the coinage was severely debased. The era was remarkable for two queens regnant, a situation without parallel in English history, and one that had immense repercussions for the coinage, not the least being the face-to-face coins of Mary and her husband Philip of Spain. It was also the era in which England followed the European example and produced very large silver coins. Two other innovations with long-term repercussions were the introduction of dates, which gradually replaced mint-marks from the middle of the 16th century, and the earliest experiments in the mechanisation of coin production. English coins were minted at Tournai during the French campaign of 1520.

Henry VII (1485–1509)

Facing Bust series (1485–1500)

Farthing, London	£145	£475	—
Halfpenny, London, open crown			
	£45	£110	—
Halfpenny, London, arched crown			
	£28	£70	£500
Halfpenny, London, shallower arches			
	£25	£55	£400
Halfpenny, Canterbury, open crown			
	£70	£160	£600
Halfpenny, Canterbury, arched crown			
	£60	£120	£500

Penny, London, facing bust			
	£160	£425	£1000
Penny, London, sovereign types from			
	£40	£90	£400
Penny, Canterbury, open crown			
	£220	£450	£1000
Penny, Canterbury, arched crown			
	£55	£140	£900
Penny, Durham, facing bust			
	£55	£145	£900
Penny, Durham, sovereign type			
	£38	£80	£250
Penny, York, facing bust	£40	£100	£300

Penny, York, sovereign type
| | £30 | £70 | £200 |

Half groat, London, open crown
| | £260 | £650 | £2000 |

Half groat, London, double arched crown
| | £38 | £85 | £400 |

Half groat, London, crown without arches
| | £30 | £75 | £280 |

Half groat, Canterbury, open crown
| | £32 | £80 | £320 |

Half groat, Canterbury, double arched crown
| | £28 | £70 | £280 |

Half groat, York, double arched crown
| | £32 | £90 | £400 |

Half groat, York, crown without arches
| | £30 | £90 | £400 |

Half groat, York, keys at side of bust
| | £30 | £80 | £320 |

| Groat, open crown | £90 | £260 | £800 |

Groat, crown with unjewelled arches
| | £70 | £160 | £600 |

Groat, crown with jewelled arches
| | £50 | £145 | £500 |

Groat, crown with one jewelled arch
| | £45 | £120 | £400 |

Groat, as above but tall thin lettering
| | £50 | £135 | £450 |

Groat, single arched crown
| | £60 | £140 | £280 |

| Half angel | £300 | £600 | £2300 |

Angel, various types from
| | £350 | £750 | £3500 |

Sovereign (20s), various types from
| | £7500 | £17500 | — |

Profile Issues (1500–09)
Obverse: right-facing bust by Alexander Brugsal. Reverse: heraldic shield.

| Half groat, London | £75 | £200 | £600 |

Half groat, London, no regnal number
| | £425 | £900 | £3000 |

| Half groat, Canterbury | £55 | £150 | £500 |

Half groat, York, two keys below shield
| | £45 | £135 | £400 |

Half groat, York, XB beside shield
| | £320 | £730 | — |

Groat, double band to crown
| | £145 | £430 | £1000 |

Groat, triple band to crown
| | £80 | £240 | £650 |

Testoon (shilling), three types from
| | £5000 | £9500 | — |

Henry VIII (1509–47)

First coinage (1509–26)
Continuing the portrait and style of Henry VII. Coins were struck at Tournai during Henry's French expedition of 1520.

Farthing, London, portcullis
| | £280 | £600 | — |

Halfpenny, London, facing bust
| | £25 | £60 | — |

Halfpenny, Canterbury, facing bust
| | £65 | £160 | — |

Penny, London, sovereign type
| | £40 | £110 | £300 |

Penny, Canterbury, various types from
| | £60 | £160 | £400 |

Penny, Durham, various types from
| | £32 | £75 | £200 |

| Half groat, London | £80 | £235 | £700 |

Half groat, Canterbury, various types from
| | £60 | £145 | £375 |

| Half groat, Tournai | £800 | £2400 | — |

Half groat, York, various types from
| | £60 | £135 | £350 |

| Half angel | £280 | £650 | £1100 |

| Angel | £330 | £750 | £1300 |

| Sovereign | £3500 | £8500 | — |

Second Coinage (1526–44)

Young (clean-shaven) portrait of Henry VIII. The initials on the gold coins refer to Henry and his wives Katherine of Aragon, Anne Boleyn and Jane Seymour, but latterly inscribed HR (Henricus Rex).

| Farthing, portcullis | £300 | £700 | — |

Halfpenny, London, various types from			
	£25	£60	—
Halfpenny, Canterbury	£35	£90	—
Halfpenny, York	£60	£140	—
Penny, sovereign type, London, various types from			
	£28	£90	£180
Penny, Canterbury, various types from			
	£70	£175	£600
Penny, Durham	£30	£80	£350
Penny, York	£140	£375	£850
Half groat, London	£40	£110	£400
Half groat, Canterbury	£40	£100	£350
Half groat, York	£9	£90	£280

Groat, London, various types from			
	£55	£140	£800
Groat, London, with Irish title HIB REX			
	£300	£750	£1350
Groat, York	£90	£225	£900

Half crown, double rose, HK			
	£345	£700	£1300
Half crown, double rose, HI			
	£375	£850	£1500
Half crown, double rose, HR			
	£500	£1000	£2500
Crown, double rose, HK	£345	£750	£1400
Crown, double rose, HA	£640	£1500	£3000
Crown, double rose, HI	£350	£750	£1400
Crown, double rose, HR	£350	£800	£1500

Crown of the rose	—	—	—
Half George noble	—	—	—
George noble	£3250	£8000	—
Half angel (3s 9d)	£700	£1450	£3000
Angel (7s 6d)	£460	£1100	£2500
Sovereign (22s 6d)	£3500	£8000	

Third coinage (1544–47).

Bearded full-face portrait.

Silver coins of this period were struck in progressively debased silver and latterly were mainly copper with a very small proportion of silver. They are generally found in poor condition and examples in EF condition are very rare. Coins were struck in London at a branch mint in Southwark, as well as at the Tower.

Farthing	—	—	—
Halfpenny, London	£30	£80	—
Halfpenny, Bristol	£70	£160	—
Halfpenny, Canterbury	£40	£110	—
Halfpenny, York	£30	£90	—
Penny, London, various types from			
	£30	£100	—
Penny, Southwark	—	—	—
Penny, Bristol	£80	£160	—

Penny, Canterbury	£85	£160	—
Penny, York	£80	£160	—
Half groat, London	£80	£175	—
Half groat, Southwark	—	—	—
Half groat, Bristol	£70	£175	—
Half groat, Canterbury	£60	£170	—

Half groat, York	£80	£180	—
Groat, London	£70	£160	—
Groat, Southwark	£80	£180	—
Groat, Bristol	£90	£200	—
Groat, Canterbury	£90	£200	—
Groat, York	£90	£200	—

Testoon, London HENRIC VIII

	£500	£1500	—

Testoon, London HENRIC 8

	£550	£1600	—
Testoon, Southwark	£550	£1600	—
Testoon, Bristol	£500	£1500	—
Half crown, London	£260	£600	£1200
Half crown, Southwark	£300	£725	£1000
Half crown, Bristol	£375	£850	£2000
Crown, London	£300	£700	£1200
Crown, Southwark	£350	£750	£1300
Crown, Bristol	£325	£700	£1200
Quarter angel	£300	£700	£1500
Half angel	£325	£700	£1200
Angel	£360	£750	£1300
Half sovereign, London	£400	£850	£2000
Half sovereign, Southwark			
	£425	£950	£2500
Half sovereign, Bristol	£630	£1450	£3000
Sovereign, London, various types from			
	£2000	£5000	£10000
Sovereign, Southwark	£1900	£4750	£9000
Sovereign, Bristol	£600	£1400	£3000

Edward VI (1547–53)

The coinage of this short reign falls into five categories. Initially base coins were struck in the name of Henry VIII but distinguished by their mint marks, followed by base coins in the name of King Edward, struck in London at the Tower as well as branch mints at Durham House (Strand) and Southwark, and also at Bristol and Canterbury. These base coins fall into three periods: April 1547 to January 1549, January 1549 to April 1550 and from then until the end of the reign. Coins of good quality alloy were also struck in 1551–53 at the Tower of London and thus overlapped the last of the base issues.

Posthumous coinage of Henry VIII (1547–51)

Roman rather than Lombardic medieval lettering.

Halfpenny, London	£50	£100	—
Halfpenny, Canterbury	£60	£110	—
Halfpenny, York	£45	£95	—
Penny, London	£60	£125	—
Penny, Southwark	£120	£500	—
Penny, Durham House	£180	£750	—
Penny, Bristol	£70	£145	—
Penny, Canterbury	£70	£140	—
Half groat, London	£60	£175	—
Half groat, Southwark	£60	£180	—

Half groat, Durham House

	£380	£700	—
Half groat, Bristol	£65	£175	—
Half groat, Canterbury	£60	£145	—
Half groat, York	£60	£175	—
Groat, London	£75	£160	—
Groat, Southwark	£80	£175	—

Groat, Durham House	£150	£340	—
Groat, Bristol	£120	£240	—
Groat, Canterbury	£80	£180	—
Groat, York	£85	£190	—
Testoon, London	£750	£1750	—
Half crown, London	£400	£850	—
Half crown, Southwark	£360	£800	—
Crown, London	£450	£900	—
Crown, Southwark	£600	£1100	—

Half sovereign, London	£400	£925	—
Half sovereign, Southwark			
	£500	£1100	—

Sovereign, London	£2500	£6500	—
Sovereign, Bristol	£3000	£7500	—

Coinage in Edward's name. First period (1547–49).

Halfpenny, London	£350	£800	—
Halfpenny, Bristol	£325	£750	—
Penny, London	£320	£875	—
Penny, Southwark	£360	£900	—
Penny, Bristol	£260	£750	—
Half groat, London	£420	£950	—
Half groat, Southwark	£400	£900	—
Half groat, Canterbury	£245	£550	—
Groat, London	£600	£1700	—
Groat, Southwark	£575	£1650	—

Shilling, Durham House	—	—	—
Half crown, London	£1750	—	—
Crown, London	£2200	—	—
Half sovereign, London	£800	£1600	—
Half sovereign, Southwark			
	£750	£1700	—

Coinage in Edward's name. Second period (1549–50).

Shilling, London	£120	£360	—
Shilling, Durham House	£160	£475	—
Shilling, Bristol	£750	£1900	—
Shilling, Canterbury	£130	£430	—
Half crown, uncrowned bust			
	£1000	£2250	—
Half crown, crowned bust			
	£800	£1800	—
Crown, uncrowned bust			
	£1000	£2250	—
Crown, crowned bust	£850	£1650	—
Half sovereign, London, uncrowned bust			
	£2500	—	—
Half sovereign, London, SCUTUM obverse			
	£725	£2100	—
Half sovereign, London, crowned bust			
	£700	£2000	—
Half sovereign, Durham House, date MDXLVIII			
	£4000	—	—
Half sovereign, Durham House, half-length bust			
	£3700	—	—

Sovereign	£2250	£6000	—

Coinage in Edward's name. Third period (1550–53). Base silver.

Farthing, London	£1000	—	—
Halfpenny, London	£200	£500	—
Penny, London	£60	£160	—
Penny, York	£55	£160	—
Shilling, London	£130	£175	—

Coinage in Edward's name. Third period (1550–53). Fine alloys.

Penny, London	£900	£2300	—

Threepence, London	£150	£500	—
Threepence, York	£350	£900	—
Sixpence, London	£120	£340	—
Sixpence, York	£145	£460	—
Shilling, London	£100	£320	£700
Half crown, (silver) galloping horse (1551–2)			
	£450	£950	—
Half crown, (silver) walking horse (1553)			
	£850	£2200	—
Half crown (gold)	£1100	£2750	—
Crown (silver), 1551–53	£500	£1100	—
Crown (gold)	£850	£2000	—
Half angel	—	—	—
Angel	£4500	£11500	—

Sovereign (20s), half-length figure			
	£1350	£3750	—
Sovereign (30s), king on throne			
	£10000	£27000	—

Mary (1553–54)

Penny, two types	£450	£1200	—
Half groat	£600	£1500	—
Groat	£90	£325	—
Half angel (5s)	£1750	£4500	—
Angel (10s)	£700	£1600	—

Ryal (15s)	£7500	£18500	—
Sovereign (1553–4) from			
	£3500	£7500	—

Mary and Philip (1554–58)

Obv. inscription: PHILIP Z MARIA. Silver coins have face to face portraits.

Penny (base metal, no portraits)			
	£60	£180	—
Penny (bust of Mary alone)			
	£300	£750	—
Half groat	£325	£850	—
Groat	£85	£300	—
Sixpence, full titles, undated			
	—	—	—

Sixpence, full titles, 1554			
	£250	£800	—
Sixpence, date below bust, 1554, 1557, from			
	£570	—	—
Sixpence, English titles only, 1555–7, from			
	£260	£800	—
Shilling, full titles, undated			
	£220	£725	—
Shilling, full titles, dated 1554			
	£250	£800	—
Shilling, as above but no XII, 1554			
	£360	£950	—
Shilling, English titles only, 1554–5, from			
	£275	£850	—
Shilling, as above but no XII			
	£375	£1000	—
Shilling, date below bust, 1554–5			
	£1200	—	—
Shilling, as above but ANG omitted			
	£2000	—	—

Half angel	£5000	—	—
Angel	£1750	£4500	—

Elizabeth I (1558–1603)

1558. Base shillings of Edward VI with countermark to reduce face value.

Portcullis (4½d)	£1400	—	—
Greyhound (2½d)	£1700	—	—

1559–61. First coinage.
Obv: Left-facing crowned bust. Rev: Heraldic shield.

Penny, wire line inner circle			
	£180	£530	—

Penny, beaded inner circle			
	£22	£70	—
Half groat, wire line inner circle			
	£160	£450	—
Half groat, beaded inner circle			
	£28	£90	—
Groat, wire line inner circle			
	£160	£460	—

Shilling, wire line inner circle

	£320	£850	—

Shilling, beaded inner circle

	£110	£220	—

Shilling, ET for Z in title	£65	£220	—

Crown gold (22 carat)

Half crown	£600	£1250	—
Crown	£625	£1400	—

Half pound (10s), various types from

	£675	£1550	—
Pound (20s)	£900	£2250	£4250

Fine gold (23½ carat)

Quarter angel	£350	£750	—
Half angel	£430	£950	—
Angel	£420	£850	—
Ryal (15s)	£400	£850	—

Sovereign (30s)	£2000	£5000	—

1560–71. Milled coinage by Eloi Mestrell.

Threefarthings	—	—	—
Half groat	£150	£475	—
Threepence, 1561-64	£80	£300	—
Groat	£130	£430	—

Sixpence, 1561–71, various dates from

	£50	£170	—
Shilling, small	£120	£360	—
Shilling, intermediate	£145	£430	—
Shilling, large	£260	£750	—

Crown gold (22 carat)

Half crown	£1600	£4250	—
Crown	£1200	£3000	—
Half pound	£1300	£3250	—

1561–82. Second hammered coinage.

This series includes several unusual denominations, intended to widen the range of the subsidiary coinage and obviate the need for farthings and halfpence which were no longer economic to produce. These new values (threefarthings, threehalfpence and threepence) were distinguished from the penny, half groat and groat by the inclusion of a rose behind the Queen's head. Dates were now generally inscribed on the reverse, above the shield, except in the case of the pennies and half groats which continued undated. In addition, however, mint marks were retained for quality control purposes and their sequence assists in the chronology of this series.

Threefarthings, 1561-2, 1568, 1572–8, 1581–2

	£65	£160	—
Penny	£22	£70	£200

Threehalfpence, 1561-2, 1564–70, 1572–9,

1581–2	£30	£90	—
Half groat	£50	£140	—

Threepence, 1561–82   £30   £160   £300

Sixpence, 1561–82   £40   £125   £300

1583–1603. Third hammered coinage. Older, more elaborate portraits.

Halfpenny, portcullis / cross and pellets

     £25   £70   £100

Penny	£20	£55	£160
Half groat	£15	£60	£200
Sixpence, 1583–1603	£40	£125	£300
Shilling	£65	£220	£400
Half crown (1601–2), two types from			
	£550	£1300	——

Crown (1601–2), two types from

       £800   £1700   ——

Stuart Kings

James I (1603–25)

Fluctuations in availability and world price of bullion in this reign resulted in a very wide and bewildering array of denominations, while political considerations also influenced the coinage. Having come from Scotland, where base metal coins were widely used, James had little compunction about solving the problem of small change by issuing base farthings, although this was contracted out to various courtiers rather than produced at the Tower mint itself.

1603–4. First coinage.

Obv: Right-facing crowned bust. Rev: Shield with arms of Scotland and Ireland incorporated. Title expressed as ANG SCO FRA ET HIB REX.

Penny	£20	£60	£160
Half groat	£25	£75	£220

Sixpence, 1603–4, several types from			
	£40	£150	£400
Shilling, several types from			
	£60	£220	£750
Half crown	£700	£2100	—
Crown	£650	£1550	£3400
22 carat gold			
Half crown	£550	£1200	£3000
Crown	£1200	£3200	£6000
Half sovereign	£1700	£4500	—

Thistle crown (4s)	£260	£475	£725
Britain crown (5s)	£220	£460	£750
Double crown (10s)	£240	£600	£1100
Unite (20s), various bust types from			
	£360	£650	£1350

1606. Fine gold (23½ carat) series.

Half angel (5s)	£1750	£4250	—
Angel (10s)	£725	£1700	—

Sovereign	£850	£2000	£4500

1604–19. Second coinage.
Title expressed as MAG BRIT FRA ET HIB REX.

Halfpenny	£12	£40	—
Penny	£15	£45	£70
Half groat, various types from			
	£20	£50	£80
Sixpence, 1604–15, various types from			
	£40	£130	—
Shilling, various types from	£60	£200	—
Half crown	£800	£2250	—
Crown	£600	£1300	—
22 carat gold			
Half crown (2s 6d)	£150	£300	—

Spur ryal (15s)	£2000	£6000	—
Rose ryal (30s)	£1000	£2500	—

1619–25. Third coinage.
Silver types as before, but laureated bust on gold coins.

Halfpenny	£15	£30	£50
Penny	£18	£35	£75
Half groat	£20	£45	£85
Sixpence, 1621–24, from	£40	£145	—
Shilling	£50	£175	—
Half crown	£145	£430	—
Half crown, plume over shield			
	£260	£400	—
Crown	£375	£800	—
Crown, plume over shield			
	£475	£1100	—
22 carat gold			
Quarter laurel (5s)	£165	£345	£650

| Half laurel (10s) | £245 | £520 | £1100 |

| Laurel (20s) | £260 | £550 | £1200 |

23½ carat gold

| Angel (10s) | £850 | £2000 | £5000 |
| Spur ryal (15s) | £2400 | £6000 | — |

| Rose ryal (30s) | £1600 | £4300 | — |

Base-metal Farthings

Up to 1613 all English coins were struck in precious metals, but by the end of the 16th century it was no longer economically viable to strike farthings in silver. In 1613 King James conferred the right to produce copper farthings on Lord Harrington and subsequently to the Duke of Lennox. Four major types were struck in this reign.

Harrington (1613) small copper with tin wash

| | £30 | £70 | £130 |

Harrington (1613) large copper, no tin surfacing	£15	£40	£90
Lennox (1614–25) IACO at 1 o'clock	£10	£25	£60
Lennox (1622–25) IACO at 7 o'clock	£22	£60	£120

Charles I (1625-49)

This is undoubtedly the most complex reign of all from every aspect, aesthetically, technically and, above all, politically. There were continuous improvements in coin design, with many new types. Hammered coinage remained dominant but there were also experiments with milled coins by Nicholas Briot. Although most coins were struck at the Tower of London, a branch mint was established at Aberystwyth to refine and coin Welsh silver, distinguished by an open book mint mark. The outbreak of the Civil War in 1642, in which Parliament gained control of the Tower mint from the outset, led to the establishment of Royalist mints at Shrewsbury, Oxford, Bristol, Chester, Exeter, Hereford, Truro and Worcester, while a number of curious makeshift coins were struck at Carlisle, Newark, Pontefract and Scarborough under siege. The manufacture of copper farthings continued under licence held by the Duchess of Richmond, Lord Maltravers and other courtiers before this was revoked by Parliament in 1644. Ironically, Parliament continued to issue coins in the King's name and bearing his effigy on the obverse, while many Royalist coins had a reverse bearing a three line promise from Charles to uphold the Protestant religion, the laws of England and the liberty of

Parliament!

1625–42. Tower Mint under Charles I.

Halfpenny	£15	£40	£60
Penny, uncrowned rose both sides			
	£15	£40	£80
Penny, 2nd bust / oval shield			
	£25	£60	£90
Penny, 3rd bust / oval shield			
	£15	£50	£80
Penny, 4th bust / oval shield			
	£15	£45	£70
Penny, 5th bust / oval shield			
	£15	£45	£65
Half groat, crowned rose both sides			
	£20	£60	£90
Half groat, 2nd bust / oval shield			
	£25	£65	£100
Half groat, 3rd bust / oval shield			
	£25	£65	£100
Half groat, 4th bust / oval or round shield, from			
	£20	£50	£80
Half groat, 5th bust / round shield			
	£30	£85	£135
Sixpence, 1st bust (1625–26), from			
	£60	£220	£400
Sixpence, 2nd bust (1626–30), from			
	£80	£240	£700

Sixpence, 3rd bust / oval shield			
	£50	£175	£600
Sixpence, 4th bust / oval shield			
	£45	£100	£400
Sixpence, 4th bust / round shield			
	£45	£100	£400
Sixpence, 5th bust / flat-topped shield			
	£40	£150	£600
Sixpence, 6th bust / flat-topped shield			
	£35	£135	£500
Shilling, 1st bust / square shield, various from			
	£60	£235	£700
Shilling, 2nd bust / square shield, various from			
	£60	£220	£650
Shilling, 3rd bust / oval shield			
	£40	£175	£650
Shilling, 4th bust / oval shield, various from			
	£40	£160	£600
Shilling, 4th bust / round shield, various from			
	£40	£150	£550
Shilling, 5th bust / square shield, various from			
	£40	£135	£400
Shilling, 6th bust / square shield, various from			
	£35	£125	£500
Half crown, 1st horseman / square shield, from			
	£120	£340	—
Half crown, 2nd horseman / oval shield, from			
	£85	£240	—
Half crown, 3rd horseman / round shield, from			
	£70	£170	—
Half crown, 4th horseman / round shield			
	£50	£130	—

Crown, 1st horseman / square shield
£400   £900   —

Crown, as above, with plumes over shield
£800   £1200   —

Crown, 2nd horseman / oval shield,
various from   £320   £800   —

22 carat gold

Crown, crowned bust / crowned shield
£250   £450   —

Double crown   £450   £900   —

Unite, various types from
£600   £1200   —

1625–44. Base metal farthings.

Richmond (1625–34), single arched crown
£7   £22   £50

Richmond (1625–34), similar but oval
£20   £55   £120

Transitional (1634) double arched crown
£18   £36   £75

Maltravers (1634–36), inner circles
£10   £27   £55

Maltravers (1634–36), double arched crown
£20   £65   £120

Rose reverse, small thick flan
£10   £20   —

Rose reverse, similar but single arched crown
£7   £25   —

Rose reverse, similar but sceptres below crown
£25   £50   —

1631–32. Milled coinage by Nicholas Briot.

Gold

Crown	£1500	—	—
Double crown	£1250	£2750	—
Angel	£3000	—	—
Unite, various types from			
	£1300	£3400	—

1638–39. Milled coinage by Nicholas Briot.

Mint-marks: anchor, anchor and B or anchor and mullet.

Sixpence	£60	£145	—
Shilling	£100	£280	—
Half crown	£220	£600	—

Mint marks: anchor or triangle over anchor.

Shilling	£325	£800	—
Half crown	£600	£1450	—

Tower Mint under Parliament (1643–49).

Mint-marks: flower and B (silver), flower and B or B alone (gold).

Penny	£45	£100	—
Half groat	£40	£90	—
Sixpence	£85	£260	—
Shilling	£180	£525	—
Half crown	£350	£800	—
Crown	£475	£1400	—

Mint marks: (P), ® or eye in sun

Penny, 7th bust	£25	£60	—
Half groat, 4th bust / round shield			
	£20	£55	—
Half groat, 7th bust / round shield			
	£25	£65	—
Sixpence, 6th bust	£70	£220	—

Sixpence, 7th bust	£65	£175	—
Sixpence, 8th bust	£120	£360	—
Shilling, 6th bust	£35	£120	—
Shilling, 7th bust	£45	£150	—
Shilling, 8th bust	£50	£180	—
Half crown, 3rd horseman	£50	£175	—
Half crown, foreshortened horse		£140	£475	—
Half crown, 5th horseman		£70	£200	—
Crown, 4th horseman	£370	£850	—
Crown, 5th horseman	£525	£1100	—

Gold

Crown	£275	£600	—
Double crown	£470	£900	—
Unite, various types from		£600	£1300	—

Provincial Mints (mainly Civil War).

Aberystwyth (1638–42). Mint-mark: open book.

Halfpenny	£160	£450	—
Penny	£55	£160	—
Half groat	£45	£110	—
Threepence	£32	£85	—
Groat	£40	£110	—
Sixpence	£220	£625	—

Shilling	£260	£730	—
Half crown, various types from		£630	£1800	—

Aberystwyth-Furnace (1647–48). Mint-mark: crown.

Penny	£640	£1700	—
Half groat	£240	£600	—
Threepence	£180	£450	—
Groat	£220	£475	—
Sixpence	£1200	£2600	—
Shilling	£2450	—	—
Half crown, various types from		£1400	£4000	—

Bristol (1643–45). Mint-marks: B, acorn or plume.

Penny	£360	£800	—
Half groat	£235	£560	—
Threepence	£160	£420	—
Groat	£145	£380	—
Sixpence	£175	£450	—
Shilling	£180	£575	—
Half crown, various types from		£220	£525	—
Gold half unite	—	—	—
Gold unite	£7000	—	—

Thomas Bushell of Lundy (1643–45). Mint-marks: A, B or plumes.

Half groat	£420	£950	—
Threepence	£120	£340	—
Groat	£120	£325	—
Sixpence	£145	£475	—

Shilling	£320	£750	—
Half crown, various types form			
	£640	£1800	—

Chester (1644). Mint-marks: Cinquefoil, plume, sideways gerb or gerbs.

Threepence	£780	£1700	—
Shilling	£850	£2300	—
Half crown, various types from			
	£640	£1500	—
Gold unite	£10000	—	—

Exeter (1643–46). Mint-marks: rose or castle.

Penny	£350	£850	—
Half groat	£170	£475	—
Threepence	£90	£220	—
Groat	£80	£200	—
Sixpence	£245	£575	—
Shilling	£280	£700	—
Half crown	£250	£600	—
Crown, various types from			
	£260	£540	—
Half pound	£5000	—	—
Gold unite	£10000	—	—

Hartlebury Castle (1646). Mint-marks: pear or three pears.

| Half crown | £1250 | £3250 | — |

Oxford (1642–46). Mint-marks: plume with band.

Penny	£145	£435	—
Half groat	£85	£245	—
Threepence	£70	£180	—
Groat	£90	£245	—
Sixpence	£170	£475	—

Shilling	£160	£460	—
Half crown	£145	£435	—
Crown	£500	£1200	—
Half pound	£575	£1250	—
Pound, several types from			
	£1200	£3000	—
Gold half unite, various types from			
	£850	£1800	—
Gold unite, various types from			
	£900	£2000	—
Gold triple unite, various types from			
	£3500	£7500	—

Shrewsbury (1642). Mint-mark: plume without band.

Shilling	£775	££200	—
Half crown	£300	£750	—
Crown	£560	£1300	—
Half pound	£550	£1200	—
Pound, various types from			
	£1300	£3000	—

Shrewsbury (Salopia) (1644). Mint-marks: helmet, lis or rose.

Half crown, various types from			
	£700	£1800	—
Gold unite	—	—	—
Gold triple unite	—	—	—

Truro (1642–43). Mint-marks: rose or bugle.

Shilling	£2450	—	—
Half crown	£635	£1750	—
Crown, various types from			
	£280	£750	—
Gold half unite	—	—	—

Welsh Borders (1644). Mint-mark: plumes.

| Half crown, horseman / Declaration | | | |
| | £600 | £1450 | — |

Worcester (1643–44). Mint-marks: castle, helmet, leopard's head, lion, two lions, lis, rose or star.

Half groat	£475	£1200	—
Threepence	£325	£650	—
Groat	£450	£1150	—
Sixpence	£735	£2000	—
Shilling, various types from			
	£900	£2600	—
Half crown, various types from			
	£560	£1700	—
Gold unite	—	—	—

York (1642–44). Mint-mark: lion.

Threepence	£45	£130	—
Sixpence	£175	£475	—
Shilling	£125	£350	—
Half crown, various types from			
	£170	£380	—

Siege Coinage
Carlisle (1644–45)

Shilling	£2500	£6000	—
Three shillings	£3500	£9000	—

Newark (1645–46)

Sixpence	£400	£800	—
Ninepence	£340	£750	—
Shilling, various types from			
	£360	£800	—
Half crown	£460	£950	—

Pontefract (1648-9)

Shilling	£900	£2250	—
Two shillings	—	—	—

Scarborough (1644-45)

Irregular pieces of silver plate were weighed and then marked with a corresponding value, hence numerous odd values. Two types feature a castle with a gateway to the left and a castle with two turrets respectively, the value being punched below. The first type ranges from 4d to 5s 8d and the second from 6d to 2s, with many odd amounts (such as 1s 4d, 2s 10d and 3s 4d) in between. We only list those pieces which come on to the market occasionally.

Shilling (type 2)	£5000	£9000	—
One shilling and threepence (type 2)			
	£4500	£8500	—
One shilling and fourpence (type 1)			
	£4250	£8500	—
Half crown (type 1)	£4900	£9000	—
Two shillings and tenpence (type 1)			
	£6000	£10000	—

Commonwealth (1649-60)

The coins produced by the Commonwealth have inscriptions in English instead of Latin which smacked of popery to the Puritans. All but the three smallest coins of this series bore a date as well as a mint mark.

1649-60.

Obv: St George's Cross. Rev: Shields of England and Ireland.

Halfpenny	£25	£60	£100
Penny	£25	£50	£120
Half groat	£30	£65	£140
Sixpence, sun mm, 1649, 165-7			
	£90	£240	£450
Sixpence, anchor mm, 1658-60			
	£130	£300	£850
Shilling, sun mm, 1649, 1651-57			
	£120	£260	£500
Shilling, anchor mm, 1658-60			
	£380	£850	£1500
Half crown, sun mm, 1649, 1651-66			
	£170	£435	£850
Half crown, anchor mm, 1658-60			
	£600	£1450	£4000

Crown, 1649, 1651–4, 1656

| | £475 | £850 | £1750 |

Gold crown, sun mm, 1649–57

| | £300 | £750 | £1400 |

Gold crown, anchor mm, 1658–60

| | £875 | £2400 | £4000 |

Double crown, sun mm, 1649–57

| | £450 | £900 | £1700 |

Double crown, anchor mm, 1660

| | £950 | £2500 | £5000 |

Unite, sun mm, 1649–57 £550 £1100 £2200

Unite, anchor mm, 1658, 1660

| | £1200 | £2750 | £6000 |

1656–58. Milled Pattern Coins.

Obv: Oliver Cromwell. Rev: Crowned shield with emblems of England, Scotland and Ireland. Engraved by Thomas Simon and struck by Pierre Blondeau. Latin inscriptions restored.

Copper farthing, 'Charitie and Change'

	£1350	£2500	—
Sixpence	—	—	—
Shilling	£220	£450	£850

Half crown, 1656, 1658, from

	£250	£500	£950
Crown, 1658	£500	£1000	£2000
Gold broad (20s), 1656	£1850	£4250	—
Fifty shillings	—	—	£18000

Restoration of the Monarchy

Charles II (1660–85)

Although equipment for the rolling, blanking and striking of coins had been installed at the Tower mint by 1656, at the Restoration coins initially reverted to the traditional hammered techniques of production and it was not until 1662 that milled coinage went into general circulation.

1660–62. Hammered coinage.

Obv: Crowned bust of Charles II facing left. Rev: Square shield. Engraved by Thomas Simon. Mint marks but no dates.

Penny	£25	£45	£85
Twopence	£20	£40	£70
Threepence	£25	£60	£100
Fourpence	£25	£65	£110
Sixpence	£80	£240	—
Shilling	£90	£260	—
Half Crown	£125	£425	—
Gold			
Crown	£550	£1450	—
Double crown	£650	£1500	—
Unite	£700	£1800	—

1663. Milled coinage.

37

Obv: Laureated bust of Charles II facing right. Rev: Crowned shields in a cruciform arrangement with sceptres in the angles (gold) or interlocking Cs in angles (large silver). Crown over C(s) (1d to 4d). Designed and engraved by John Roettiers.

Penny, undated	£25	£35	£80
Penny, 1670–84, from	£22	£40	£80
Twopence, undated	£25	£35	£80
Twopence, 1668, 1670–84, from	£28	£55	£65
Threepence, undated	£20	£35	£80
Threepence, 1670–84, from	£18	£25	£70
Fourpence, undated	£25	£45	£90
Fourpence, 1670–84, from	£20	£30	£65
Sixpence, 1674–84, from	£45	£110	£300
Shilling, 1st bust, 1663–69, from	£50	£125	——
Shilling, elephant below bust (1666)	£200	£550	£1600
Shilling, 2nd bust, 1669–74, from	£60	£150	£600
Shilling, plumes below bust and centre of reverse, from	£160	£350	£1100
Shilling, 3rd bust, 1674–83, from	£70	£220	£650
Shilling, plume below bust, from	£160	£400	£1200
Shilling, elephant and castle below bust (1681)	£700	——	——
Shilling, 4th bust, 1683–4, from	£120	£340	£900
Half crown, 1st bust, 1663, two types from	£65	£300	£1250
Half crown, 2nd bust, 1664	£70	£360	£1800
Half crown, 3rd bust, 1666–72, from	£50	£150	£800
Half crown, elephant below bust, 1666	£175	£450	£260(0)
Half crown, 4th bust, 1672–84, from	£55	£150	£80(0)
Half crown, plume below bust, 1673, 1683 from	£850	—	
Half crown, elephant and castle below bust 1681	£600	—	—
Crown, 1st bust, 1662–3, several types from	£65	£280	£210(0)
Crown, 2nd bust, 1664–71, from	£65	£300	£250(0)
Crown, elephant below bust, 1666	£180	£525	£350(0)
Crown, 3rd bust, 1671–79, from	£65	£250	£165(0)
Crown, 4th bust, 1679–84, from	£65	£250	£180(0)
Crown, elephant and castle below bust, 1681	£500	£1100	—
Half guinea, 1st bust, 1669–72, from	£185	£460	£200(0)
Half guinea. 2nd bust, 1672–84, from	£180	£460	£200(0)
Half guinea, elephant and castle (1676, 78, 80, 82, 84) from	£350	£700	£275(0)
Guinea, 1st bust, 1663	£550	£1700	—
Guinea, elephant below bust	£550	£1600	—
Guinea, 2nd bust, 1664	£400	£1250	—
Guinea, 3rd bust, 1664–72, from	£280	£800	£325(0)
Guinea, elephant below bust (1665, 1668), from	£320	£800	£325(0)
Guinea, 4th bust, 1672–84, from	£200	£550	£250(0)
Guinea, elephant below bust (1677–8), from	£2500	—	—
Guinea, elephant and castle (1674–84, from	£325	£850	£325(0)
Two guineas, 1st bust, 1664–71, from	£430	£1350	—
Two guineas, elephant below bust (1664)	£400	£850	£435(0)
Two guineas, 2nd bust, 1675–84, from	£450	£1100	£400(0)
Two guineas, elephant and castle below bust (1676–84) from	£450	£1300	—
Five guineas, 1st bust, 1668–78, from	£1000	£2000	£700(0)
Five guineas, elephant below bust (1668, 69, 75), from	£1000	£2000	£750(0)

Five guineas, 2nd bust, 1678–84, from
| | £1050 | £2000 | £6500 |

Five guineas, elephant and castle below bust (1680–3) from
| | £1200 | £2000 | £6500 |

1672-85. Base metal coinage.

Obv: Laureated bust of Charles II facing right. Rev: Britannia.

Copper farthing, 1672–6, 1679, several types from
| | £5 | £60 | £350 |

Tin farthing, 1684–5, several types from
| | £50 | £250 | — |

Copper halfpenny, 1672–3, 1675 several types from
| | £25 | £80 | £550 |

James II (1685–89)

1685–87. Base-metal coinage.

Obv: Right-facing cuirassed bust (farthing) or draped bust (halfpenny). Rev: Seated Britannia. Tin with central copper plug.

Farthing, 1685–87, from £60 £800 —

Farthing, draped bust, 1687
| | £150 | £350 | — |

Halfpenny, 1685–87, from
| | £100 | £225 | £1000 |

1685–88. Gold and silver coinage.

Obv: Laureated bust facing left. Rev: Crowned shields in cruciform arrangement with sceptres in angles (gold), without sceptres (large silver) and crown over I(s) on 1d to 4d. Engraved by James Roettier.

Penny, 1685–88, from £25 £35 £75
Twopence, 1686–88, from £22 £35 £75
Threepence, 1685–88, from
| | £20 | £28 | £70 |

Fourpence, 1686–88, from
| | £25 | £40 | £80 |

Sixpence, 1st shields, 1686–87, from
| | £80 | £180 | £460 |

Sixpence, 2nd shields, 1687–88, from
| | £75 | £190 | £500 |

Shilling, 1685–88, from £80 £200 £520
Shilling, plume in centre of reverse, 1685
| | — | — | — |

Half crown, 1st bust, 1685–86, from
| | £75 | £200 | £650 |

Half crown, 2nd bust, 1687–88, from
| | £75 | £200 | £750 |

Crown, 1st bust, 1686, two types from
| | £90 | £335 | £1300 |

Crown, 2nd bust, 1687–88, from
| | £75 | £300 | £950 |

Half guinea, 1686–88, from
| | £250 | £550 | £2250 |

Half guinea, elephant and castle below bust, 1686
| | £460 | £1450 | £4000 |

Guinea, 1st bust, 1685–86, from
| | £240 | £550 | £2500 |

Guinea, elephant and castle below bust, 1685–66, from
| | £280 | £600 | £2750 |

Guinea, 2nd bust, 1686–88, from
£250   £600   £2500
Guinea, elephant and castle, 1686-88, from
£300   £625   £2500
Two guineas, 1687–88, from
£500   £1100   £4000
Five guineas, 1686–88, from
£1000   £2000   £6000
Five guineas, elephant and castle, 1687–88,
from   £1050   £2100   £6500

William and Mary (1688–94)

Obv: Conjoined busts facing right. Rev: Crowned shields (gold), cruciform shields with WM monograms in the angles (large silver), crown over Arabic numerals (1d to 4d) and seated Britannia (base metal). Engraved by James and Norbert Roettier.
Farthing, tin, small draped busts, 1689
£320   —   —
Farthing, tin, large cuirassed busts, 1690–2, from   £100   £220   £825
Farthing, copper, 1694, several varieties from
£30   £70   £500
Halfpenny, tin, small draped busts, 1689
£300   —   —
Halfpenny, tin, large cuirassed busts,
1690–2, from   £110   £270   £1000
Halfpenny, copper, 1694   £30   £90   £650
Penny, legend continuous over heads, 1689
£270   £300   £480
Penny, legend broken over heads, 1690–94,
from   £40   £50   £90
Twopence, 1689–94, from £20   £30   £75

Threepence, 1st busts, no tie, 1689–91, from
£25   £40   £8(
Threepence, 2nd busts with tie, 1691–4, from
£40   £80   £11(
Fourpence, 1st busts, no tie, 1689–94, from
£20   £45   £9(
Fourpence, 2nd busts with tie, 1692–94, from
£15   £30   £8(
Sixpence, 1693–94, from £80   £180   £47!
Shilling, 1693–94, from   £85   £230   £52(
Half crown, 1st busts, broad shield, 1689
£55   £125   £45(
Half crown, 1st busts, narrow shield, 1689–90,
from   £60   £140   £50(
Half crown, 2nd busts, 1691–93, from
£75   £175   £55(
Crown, 1691–2, from   £175   £450   £185(
Half guinea, 1st busts, 1689
£300   £600   £200(
Half guinea, 2nd busts, 1690–4, from
£300   £650   £210(
Half guinea, elephant below busts, 1692
—   —   —
Half guinea, elephant and castle below busts
1691–2, from   £300   £600   £185(
Guinea, 1689–94, from   £260   £625   £250(
Guinea, elephant and castle below busts,
1689–94, from   £275   £650   £250(
Guinea, elephant below bust, 1692–93, from
£500   £1100   £350(
Two guineas, 1693–94, from
£475   £1200   £350(
Two guineas, elephant and castle below busts,
1691–4 from   £530   £1300   £385(
Five guineas, 1691–94, from
£1000   £1950   £600(
Five guineas, elephant and castle, 1691–94,
from   £1100   £2000   £650(

William III (1694–1702)

letter below the bust. The first provenance marks appeared in this period, coins with roses between the heraldic shields denoting silver from mines in the west of England while those with plumes in the angles or below the bust denote Welsh silver.

Obv: Right-facing laureated bust. Rev: Cruciform arms, etc. Engraved by Johann Croker.

Farthing, date in exergue, 1695–1700, from	£22	£75	£380
Farthing, date after BRITANNIA, 1698–99, from	£28	£80	£460
Halfpenny, date in exergue, 1695–98, from	£30	£80	£440
Halfpenny, date after BRITANNIA, 1698–99, from	£30	£120	—
Halfpenny, Britannia with right hand on knee, 1699–1701	£30	£90	£450
Penny, 1698–1701	£36	£55	£85
Twopence, crown to edge of coin, large 2, 1699–1701, from	£27	£40	£80
Twopence, crown within circle, small 2, 1698–1701, from	£30	£50	£90
Threepence, 1698–1701, from	£30	£45	£80
Fourpence, 1698–1702, from	£30	£45	£80
Sixpence, 1st bust, early harp, 1695–6	£18	£55	£150
Sixpence, Bristol, 1696	£22	£55	£200
Sixpence, Chester, 1696	£22	£55	£200
Sixpence, Exeter, 1696	£22	£55	£210
Sixpence, Norwich, 1696	£22	£55	£200
Sixpence, York, small y, 1696	£22	£55	£200
Sixpence, York, capital Y, 1696	£25	£70	£320
Sixpence, 1st bust, later harp, large crowns, 1696	£35	£100	£300
Sixpence, Bristol, 1696	£30	£100	£280
Sixpence, Chester, 1696	£45	£150	£475
Sixpence, Norwich, 1696	£40	£145	£600
Sixpence, 2nd bust, 1696–7, from	£175	£400	—

The chief event of William's solo reign was the wholesale recoinage of 1696, calling in coins which were clipped and badly worn. For this purpose branch mints in Bristol, Chester, Exeter, Norwich and York were established and coins struck there are identified by an initial

Sixpence, 2nd bust, Bristol, 1697
£25 £60 £200

Sixpence, 2nd bust, Chester, 1697
£25 £60 £220

Sixpence, 2nd bust, Exeter, 1697
£25 £60 £210

Sixpence, 2nd bust, Norwich, 1697
£25 £60 £210

Sixpence, 2nd bust, York (y), 1697
£25 £60 £225

Sixpence, 3rd bust, large crowns, 1697–1701,
from £12 £35 £110

Sixpence, 3rd bust, Bristol, 1697
£22 £65 £280

Sixpence, 3rd bust, Chester, 1697
£25 £90 £300

Sixpence, 3rd bust, Exeter, 1697
£25 £80 £260

Sixpence, 3rd bust, York (Y), 1697
£30 £90 £300

Sixpence, plumes in angles, 1698–99, from
£35 £90 £325

Sixpence, roses in angles, 1699
£45 £120 £325

Sixpence, plume below bust, 1700
£600 — —

Shilling, 1st bust, 1695–97, from
£20 £55 £150

Shilling, 1st bust, Bristol, 1696–97
£30 £70 £240

Shilling, 1st bust, Chester, 1696–97
£30 £70 £250

Shilling, 1st bust, Exeter, 1696–97
£30 £75 £260

Shilling, 1st bust, Norwich, 1696–97
£30 £75 £270

Shilling, 1st bust, York (y), 1696–7
£30 £80 £275

Shilling, 1st bust, York (Y), 1696–7
£25 £85 £300

Shilling, 2nd bust, hair across breast, 1696
— — —

Shilling, 3rd bust, 1697, two types from
£25 £75 £160

Shilling, 3rd bust, Bristol, 1697, two types from
£25 £75 £270

Shilling, 3rd bust, Chester, 1696–97, from
£30 £75 £300

Shilling, 3rd bust, Exeter, 1697, two types from
£30 £75 £300

Shilling, 3rd bust, Norwich, 1697
£30 £70 £275

Shilling, 3rd bust York (y), 1696–97, from
£30 £70 £260

Shilling, 3rd bust, plumes in angles, 1698
£60 £180 £500

Shilling, 4th bust, 'flaming hair', 1698–99
£85 £250 £750

Shilling, 5th bust, 1699–1701, from
£35 £75 £200

Shilling, 5th bust, plumes in angles,
1699, 1701, from £60 £170 £450

Shilling, 5th bust, roses in angles, 1699
£60 £180 £550

Shilling, 5th bust, plume below bust, 1700
£800 — —

Half crown, 1st bust, small shields, 1696
£30 £100 £260

Half crown, 1st bust, small shields, Bristol,
1696 £40 £120 £350

Half crown, 1st bust, small shields, Chester,
1696 £40 £130 £400

Half crown, 1st bust, small shields, Exeter, 1696
£40 £140 £375

Half crown, 1st bust, small shields, Norwich,
1696 £40 £140 £365

Half crown, 1st bust, small shields, York (y),
1696 £40 £140 £380

Half crown, 1st bust, large shields, 1st harp,
1696 £30 £75 £260
Bristol, 1696 £35 £120 £365
Chester, 1696 £35 £120 £385
Exeter, 1696 £35 £120 £450
Norwich, 1696 £60 £170 £500
York (y), 1696 £40 £125 £375

Half crown, 1st bust, large shields, ordinary
harp, 1696–7 £65 £180 £500
Chester, 1696–97, from £65 £220 £550
Exeter, 1696–97, from £60 £180 £500
Norwich, 1696–97, from
£40 £140 £375
York (y), 1697 £40 £140 £375

Half crown, modified shields, 1698–1701, from
£40 £170 £500

Half crown, elephant and castle below bust,
1701

Half crown, plumes in angles, 1701
£70 £220 £575

Crown, 1st bust, 1695–96 £55 £160 £550

Crown, 2nd bust (hair across breast), 1696
— — —

Crown, 3rd bust, 1st harp, 1696
£50 £150 £500

Crown, 3rd bust, 2nd harp, 1697
£200 £700 £1100

Crown, 3rd bust, 3rd harp, 1700
£80 £200 £660

Half guinea, early harp, 1695

    £160   £375   £1600

Half guinea, early harp, elephant and castle, 1695–96, from

    £220   £500   £2000

Half guinea, late harp, 1697–1701, from

    £160   £400   £1500

Half guinea, late harp, elephant and castle, 1698

    £350   £700   £2300

Guinea, 1st bust, 1695–97, from

    £200   £450   £1800

Elephant and castle, 1695–96, from

    £335   £600   £2000

Guinea, 2nd bust, human-headed harp, 1697-1700, from

    £220   £475   £1800

Elephant and castle, 1697–1700, from

    £350   £650   £2500

Guinea, 2nd bust, large lettering and date, 1698

    £225   £475   £2000

Guinea, 3rd bust 'fine work', 1701

    £450   £1100   £3000

Two guineas, 3rd bust 'fine work', 1701

    £600   £1750   £4250

Five guineas, 1st bust, 1699–1700, from

    £1000   £2000   £4500

Five guineas, elephant and castle below bust, 1699

    £1100   £2000   £4500

Five guineas, 2nd bust 'fine work', 1701

    £1200   £2350   £5000

Anne (1702–14)

The Act of Union (1707) which united England and Scotland resulted in the demise of the Scottish parliament and the Edinburgh mint. Numismatically these changes are reflected in the alteration in the royal arms which henceforward showed the three lions of England and the lion rampant of Scotland dimidiated and conjoined. The Edinburgh mint continued in operation until 1709 but between 1707 and the latter date it struck coins of the English pattern, identified by the initial E below the Queen's bust. In addition to the rose and plume provenance marks, coins were inscribed VIGO below the bust to denote gold or silver bullion seized from the Spaniards during the Anglo-Dutch expedition that raided the Spanish port in 1702. Subsidiary copper coinage was confined to farthings minted only in 1714.

1702–7. Before Union with Scotland.

Obv: Left-facing bust of Queen Anne. Rev: crowned heraldic shields of England, Scotland, France and Ireland, with sceptres in the angles (gold), no sceptres (silver sixpence to crown) or crowned numerals of value (penny to fourpence). Engraved by Johann Croker.

Penny, 1703–13, various dates from

    £30   £40   £75

Twopence, 1st bust, crown to edge of coin, 1703–8   £20   £35   £70

Twopence, 2nd bust, crown within circle, 1708–9   £15   £30   £60

Threepence, broad bust, 1703

    £30   £45   £85

Threepence, taller, narrower bust, 1704–6, from

    £25   £30   £70

Threepence, large bust, 1707–13, from

    £20   £35   £70

Fourpence, small bust, 1703–4, from

    £30   £50   £90

Fourpence, large bust, 1704–10, from

    £25   £45   £85

Fourpence, large crown, pearls on arch, 1710, 1713   £22   £35   £65

Fourpence, large bust with fine hair, 1710, 1713

    £25   £40   £85

Sixpence, VIGO below bust, 1703

    £25   £55   £160

Sixpence, plain, 1705   £40   390   £250

Sixpence, plumes in angles, 1705

    £25   £60   £200

Sixpence, rose and plumes in angles, 1705, 1707   £25   £65   £210

Shilling, 1st bust, 1702   £30   £80   £250

Shilling, plumes in angles, 1702

    £35   £85   £270

Shilling, VIGO below bust, 1702
                £35   £80   £250
Shilling, 2nd bust, VIGO, 1703
                £35   £80   £250
Shilling, 2nd bust plain, 1704–5, from
                £40 £120   £320
Shilling, 2nd bust, plumes in angles,
1704–5, from   £35 £110   £320
Shilling, 2nd bust, rose and plumes in angles,
1705–7   £30 £110   £320
Half crown, plain, 1703 £125   £400   ——
Half crown, VIGO below bust, 1703
                £50 £135   £420
Half crown, plumes in angles, 1704–5, from
                £50 £150   £500
Half crown, rose and plumes in angles, 1706-7
                £40 £145   £370
Crown, VIGO below bust, 1703
              £130   £400 £1200
Crown, plumes in angles, 1705
              £240   £575 £1800
Crown, roses and plumes in angles, 1706–7
              £140   £350 £1000
Half guinea, 1702, 1705 £250   £600 £2400
Half guinea, VIGO below bust, 1703
             £2400 £5000   ——
Guinea, 1702, 1705–7, from
              £275   £750 £2750
Guinea, VIGO below bust
             £3750 £8000   ——
Five guineas, 1705–6 £1000 £2000 £5000
Five guineas, VIGO below bust, 1703
            £6500 £16000 £42000

After Union with Scotland, 1707–14.

Obv: Left-facing bust of Queen Anne. Rev: as before but dimidiated lions of England and Scotland in crowned shields of first and third quarters. Star of the Garter in centre. Coins with the initial letter E (Edinburgh) below the queen's bust are listed at the end of the Scottish section.

Sixpence, plain, 1707–8, 1711, from
              £20   £40   £140
Sixpence, plumes in angles, 1703
              £25   £60   £190
Sixpence, plumes and roses in angles, 1710
              £25   £60   £200
Shilling, 3rd bust, 1707–9, 1711, from
              £25   £60   £150
Shilling, 3rd bust, plumes in angles, 1707–8
              £30   £85   £360
Shilling, 4th bust, roses and plumes in angles,
1710–14   £35 £100   £300
Shilling, 4th bust, plain, 1711
              £20   £35   £110
Half crown, plain, 1707–9, 1713, from
              £35 £100   £275
Half crown, plumes in angles, 1708
              £40 £110   £385
Half crown, roses and plumes in angles, 1710,
1712–14   £40 £110   £375
Crown, 2nd bust, plain, 1707–8 from
              £80 £240   £775
Crown, 2nd bust, plumes in angles, 1708
             £125   £345 £1000

Crown, 3rd bust, roses and plumes in angles,
1713 £145 £420 £1100
Half guinea, 1707–14, from
£170 £399 £1200
Guinea, 1st bust, 1707–8, from
£650 — —
Guinea, 1st bust, elephant and castle below,
1707-8 £850 £1600 —
Guinea, 2nd bust, 1707–9, from
£700 £1250 £3250
Guinea, 2nd bust, elephant and castle, 1708-9
£700 £1250 £3250
Guinea, 3rd bust, 1710–14
£180 £375 £1600
Two guineas, 1709, 1711, 1713–14, from
£450 £1000 £3000
Five guineas, post-Union shields, 1706
£1000 £1650 £5000
Five guineas, narrow shields, tall crowns, 1709
£1100 £1800 £5500
Five guineas, broader shields, 1711, 1713–14
£1000 £1700 £5000

1714. Base metal coinage.

Obv: Left-facing bust of Queen Anne. Rev:
Britannia.
Farthing, date in exergue £100 £250 £500

George I (1714–27)

On the death of Queen Anne the crown passed
to her kinsman, George Louis, Elector of
Hanover (descended from the sister of Charles
I, Elizabeth, the 'Winter Queen' of Bohemia).
The change of dynasty was signified in the elaborate set of initials on the obverse to accommo-
date the new monarch's many titles, and the
replacement of one of the Anglo-Scottish
shields by one showing the arms of Hanover,
Brunswick and Luneberg with an electoral

crown of the Holy Roman Empire superimposed in the centre. The system of provenance
marks to denote the source of silver was
extended. Coins with the initials W.C.C. below
the king's bust and plumes and interlocking CC
on the reverse indicate silver supplied by the
Welsh Copper Company. Roses and plumes in
alternate angles on the reverse identify silver
supplied by the Company for Smelting Pit Coale
and Sea Coale. Coins with the initials S.S.C.
signify bullion supplied by the ill-starred South
Sea Company shortly before it crashed spectac-
ularly in 1723.

Obv: Right-facing laureated bust. Rev: Crowned
shields containing the arms of Great Britain,
fleur de lis (France), harp (Ireland) and arms of
Brunswick and Luneberg. Crossed sceptres
(gold), provenance marks in angles or plain
(silver sixpence to crown) and crowned numerals (penny to fourpence). Engraved by Johann
Croker and John R. Ochs.
Farthing, small thick flan, 1717
£32 £110 £420
Farthing, larger, thinner flan, 1719–24, from
£20 £60 £220
Halfpenny, small thick flan, 1717–18, from
£30 £75 £300
Halfpenny, larger, thinner flan, 1717, 1719-24,
from £25 £65 £300
Penny, 1716, 1718, 1720, 1723, 1727–7, from
£15 £25 £40
Twopence, 1717, 1721, 1723, 1726–7, from
£18 £30 £50
Threepence, 1717, 1721, 1723, 1727, from
£30 £40 £75
Fourpence, 1717, 1721, 1723, 1727, from
£25 £45 £75
Sixpence, rose and plumes, 1717, 1720, from
£40 £110 £300
Sixpence, SSC in angles, 1723
£15 £40 £110

Sixpence, small roses and plumes, 1726
£70 £160 £460
Shilling, 1st bust, roses and plumes, 1715–23,
from £30 £70 £240
Shilling, 1st bust, no marks, 1720–21, from
£25 ££60 £200
Shilling, 1st bust, SSC in angles, 1723
£15 £40 £120
Shilling, 2nd bust, SSC in angles, 1723
£25 £70 £260
Shilling, 2nd bust, roses and plumes, 1723–27,
from £35 £90 £275
Shilling, 2nd bust, W.C.C. below bust, 1723–26,
from £220 £500 £2000
Half crown, roses and plumes, 1715, 1717,
1720, from £135 £325 £800
Half crown, SSC in angles, 1723
£140 £350 £750
Half crown, small roses and plumes, 1726
£800 £1100 —
Crown, roses and plumes, 1716, 1718, 1720,
1726, from £240 £460 £1500
Crown, SSC in angles, 1723
£275 £460 £1300
Quarter guinea (7s 6d), 1718
£60 £100 £235
Half guinea, 1st bust, 1715, 1717–24, from
£160 £320 £1000
Half guinea, 1st bust, elephant and castle,
1726 £1000 £1500 —
Half guinea, 2nd bust, 1725–27, from
£160 £320 £1100
Guinea, 1st bust, PR(ince) EL(ector) in title,
1714 £550 £950 £3000
Guinea, 2nd bust, 1715 £200 £360 £1650
Guinea, 3rd bust, 1715–16
£210 £375 £1750
Guinea, 4th bust, 1716–23, from
£200 £370 £1700
Guinea, 4th bust, elephant and castle, 1721-22
— — —
Guinea, 5th bust, 1723–27, from
£200 £370 £1750
Guinea, 5th bust, elephant and castle, 1726
£500 £1450 —
Two guineas, 1717, 1720, 1726, from
£450 £1200 £4000
Five guineas, 1716–17, 1720, 1726, from
£1200 £2750 £7000

George II (1727–60)

During this reign there was a chronic shortage of silver which was only coined sporadically. The seizure of Spanish gold and silver by Admiral Anson during his voyage round the world (1740–44) resulted in coins with the name LIMA inscribed below the king's bust (1745–46). Coins minted from bullion supplied by the East India Company were denoted by initials. The style of gold, silver and copper coinage continued as before, although the florid embellishment of the heraldic shields on the gold coinage reflected the Baroque fashion of the period. The chief difference between the coins of George II and his father was the abandonment of the string of initials on the obverse and their transfer to the reverse.

1727–45. Young Head Coinage.

Obv: Left-facing laureated bust by Johann Croker. Rev: Crowned shield (gold), cruciform shields (silver sixpence to crown), crowned numerals (penny to fourpence) and Britannia (copper) by John Sigismund Tanner and J.R. Ochs, Junior.
Farthing, 1730–37, 1739, from
£12 £30 £160
Halfpenny, 1729–39, from £15 £45 £170
Penny, date over small crown, 1729, 1731, from
£22 £32 £50
Penny, large crown dividing date, 1732–60,
from £22 £40 £80
Twopence, small crown, 1729, 1731, from
£25 £40 £50
Twopence, large crown, 1732–60, from
£15 £22 £40

Threepence, 1st crown, 1729
£15 £25 £40
Threepence, 2nd crown, 1731–2, from
£27 £40 £60
Threepence, 3rd crown, 1735–60, from
£22 £35 £65
Fourpence, 1st crown, 1729, 1731, from
£27 £40 £65
Fourpence, 2nd crown, 1732–60, from
£22 £35 £60
Sixpence, plain, 1728 £40 £95 £320
Sixpence, plumes, 1728 £30 £75 £240
Sixpence, roses and plumes, 1728, 1731–36,
from £25 £50 £165
Sixpence, roses, 1739, 1741, from
£20 £50 £125
Shilling, roses and plumes, 1727–29, 1731–2,
from £35 £100 £260
Shilling, large lettering, rose and plumes,
1734–7 £32 £75 £100
Shilling, plain, 1728 £40 £110 £350
Shilling, roses, 1739, 1741, from
£30 £60 £175
Half crown, roses and plumes, 1731–2, 1734–6
£60 £140 £425
Half crown, roses, 1739, 1741, from
£55 £130 £370
Crown, roses and plumes, 1732, 1734–36, from
£145 £320 £750
Crown, roses, 1739, 1741, from
£130 £320 £675
Half guinea, 1728–39, from
£175 £375 £1500
Half guinea, E.I.C. below bust, 1729–32, 1739,
from £180 £400 £2000
Half guinea, intermediate head, 1740, 1743,
1745–6 £180 £400 £1500
Half guinea, LIMA below bust, 1745
£575 £1500 £3000
Guinea, 1st bust, small lettering, large shield,
1727 £500 £850 £2450
Guinea, larger lettering, small shield, 1727–28
£350 £650 £2000
Guinea, narrower bust, 1729–32, from
£190 £400 £2000
Guinea, E.I.C. below bust, 1729–32, from
£300 £400 £2400
Guinea, larger lettering, 1732–38, from
£200 £350 £1750
Guinea, E.I.C. below bust, 1732
£325 £950 £2500
Guinea, intermediate head, 1739–41, 1743,
from £200 £400 £1600

Guinea, E.I.C. below bust, 1739
£225 £460 £2400
Guinea large lettering, GEORGIUS, 1745
£220 £400 £2000
Guinea, GEORGIVS, 1745
£200 £350 £1500
Two guineas, round-arched crown, 1734
£750 £2000 —
Two guineas, pointed arches, 1735, 1738–9
£350 £700 £1750
Two guineas, intermediate head, 1739–40, from
£300 £600 £1500
Five guineas, 1729 £1000 £1650 £4000
Five guineas, E.I.C. below bust, 1729
£1000 £1700 £4200
Five guineas, revised shield, 1731, 35, 38, 1741
£1000 £1750 £4500

1740–60. Old Head coinage.

Obv: Left-facing bust by John Sigismund
Tanner. Rev: Similar to first series.
Farthing, GEORGIUS, 1741, 1744, from
£15 £45 £180
Farthing, GEORGIVS, 1746, 1749, 1750, 1754
£10 £20 £130
Halfpenny, GEORGIUS, 1740–45, from
£12 £40 £145
Halfpenny, GEORGIVS, 1746–54, from
£12 £40 £145
Sixpence, roses, 1743, 1745, from
£12 £35 £110

Sixpence, LIMA below bust, 1745–6
| | £12 | £35 | £90 |

Sixpence, plain, 1750–51, 1757–58, from
| | £10 | £20 | £50 |

Shilling, roses, 1743, 1745, 1747, from
| | £15 | £40 | £135 |

Shilling, LIMA below bust, 1745–6, from
| | £15 | £45 | £140 |

Shilling, plain, 1750-51, 1758, from
| | £7 | £25 | £70 |

Half crown, roses, 1743, 1745
| | £35 | £70 | £210 |

Half crown, LIMA below bust, 1745–46
| | £30 | £60 | £200 |

Half crown, plain, 1750–51, from
| | £60 | £200 | £600 |

Crown, roses, 1743 £130 £280 £650

Crown, LIMA below bust, 1746
| | £135 | £300 | £700 |

Crown, plain, 1750–51, from
| | £200 | £380 | £950 |

Half guinea, 1747–60, from
| | £125 | £230 | £850 |

Guinea, 1747–60 £200 £350 £1250

Two guineas, 1748, 1753, from
| | £325 | £750 | £2000 |

Five guineas, LIMA below bust, 1746
| | £1000 | £1750 | £4500 |

Five guineas, plain, 1748, 1753
| | £950 | £1700 | £4200 |

George III (1760–1820)

One of the longest and most momentous reigns in British history, it witnessed the loss of the American colonies but spectacular gains in Canada, India, Ceylon, Australia, South Africa and the East Indies which saw the British Empire emerge as the greatest world power by the end of the reign. It was a period dominated by wars with France, notably the 22 years of the French Revolutionary and Napoleonic Wars. Ironically, it was during the brief respite offered by the Peace of Amiens (1802) that British coins dropped the French title and fleur de lis emblem which had been inscribed since the 14th century. Monetary and economic problems resulted in the even more spasmodic production of silver coins, and the adoption of third and quarter guineas, tariffed at 7s and 5s 3d respectively, in place of large silver pieces. Latterly, however, even gold was in short supply. Small silver coins virtually disappeared,

being restricted to the annual Maundy ceremony, but it was not until 1797 that the government sanctioned an issue of copper pennies and twopences. Following the precedent of the first farthings in the reign of James I, the contract was farmed out to Messrs Boulton and Watt at their Soho Mint in Birmingham. Relatively few farthings or halfpence were minted in this period, and the gap was largely filled by tokens produced by merchants, shopkeepers and private banks. In 1804 the Bank of England produced silver tokens, consisting mainly of Spanish dollars countermarked with the king's effigy, followed by more elaborate issues, including denominations of 9d, 18d and 3s (1811–16). In 1816, however, the coinage was completely changed and thereafter the nominal value was less than the intrinsic value of the metal. The mint moved out of the Tower of London into new premises on nearby Tower Hill, equipped with steam-powered presses. The guinea (21s) was replaced by the sovereign (20s) and the weights and specifications of the silver coins were reduced. Theoretically at least, the shilling of 1816 remained legal tender (as the equivalent of the 5p coin) until 1990. Due to the piecemeal nature of the coinage prior to the reforms of 1816 it is impossible to separate.

1761–1773. Young Head Coinage.

Obv: Right-facing laureated bust by Richard Yeo. Rev: Crowned shield by John Sigismund Tanner (gold). Silver and copper reverses as for George II.

Farthing, 1771, 1773–75, from
| | £12 | £25 | £95 |

Halfpenny, 1770–75, from £10 £30 £125

Penny, 1763, 66, 70, 72, 76, 79–81, 84, 1786, from
| | £14 | £20 | £30 |

Twopence, 1763, 66, 70, 80, 84, 1786, from
| | £15 | £22 | £35 |

Threepence, 1762-3, 1765–6, 70, 72, 80, 84, 1786, from
| | £10 | £18 | £32 |

Fourpence, 1763, 1765–6, 70, 72, 76, 80, 84, 1786, from
| | £20 | £30 | £45 |

Shilling, 'Northumberland' type, 1763

| | £170 | £300 | £500 |
| Quarter guinea, 1762 | £45 | £100 | £235 |

Half guinea, 1st bust, 1762–63, from

| | £210 | £400 | £1100 |

Half guinea, 2nd bust, 1764–9, 1772–5

| | £150 | £260 | £500 |

Half guinea, 3rd bust, 1774–75, from

| | £260 | £500 | £1500 |

| Guinea, 1st bust, 1761 | £360 | £800 | £2350 |

Guinea, 2nd bust, 1763–64, from

| | £220 | £500 | £1500 |

Guinea, 3rd bust, 1765–73, from

| | £150 | £320 | £750 |

Two guineas, pattern only, 1768

| | — | — | £12000 |

Five guineas, pattern only, 1770

| | — | — | £35000 |

1773–86. Fourth Head Coinage.

Obv: Right-facing bust by Thomas Pingo. Rev: Baroque shield as previous designs.

Half guinea, 1775–79, 1781–86, from

| | £70 | £135 | £300 |

Guinea, 1774–79, 1781-86, from

| | £100 | £160 | £400 |

Two guineas, pattern only, 1773, 1777

| | — | — | £12000 |

Five guineas, pattern only, 1773, 1777

| | — | — | £12000 |

1787–99. Fifth Head Coinage.

Obv: Right-facing bust by Lewis Pingo. Rev: Crowned spade-shaped shield (gold) by Pingo. Other coins with reverses as before.

| Penny, 'wire money' thin 1, 1792 | £5 | £12 | £30 |

Penny, normal 1, 1795, 1800, from

| | £4 | £10 | £20 |

Twopence, 'wire money' thin 2, 1792

| | £8 | £15 | £35 |

Twopence, normal 2, 1795, 1800, from

| | £10 | £18 | £30 |

Threepence, 'wire money', thin 3, 1792

| | £12 | £25 | £40 |

Threepence, normal 3, 1795, 1800, from

| | £15 | £20 | £30 |

Fourpence, 'wire money', thin 4, 1792

| | £20 | £40 | £55 |

Fourpence, normal 4, 1795, 1800, from

| | £15 | £25 | £30 |

Sixpence, without hearts in Hanoverian shield, 1787

| | £8 | £17 | £35 |

| Sixpence, with hearts, 1787 | £8 | £18 | £40 |

Shilling, without hearts, 1787, various from

| | £6 | £15 | £50 |

| Shilling, with hearts, 1787 | £7 | £16 | £50 |

Shilling, 'Dorrien & Magens' type, 1798

| | — | — | £3400 |

Third guinea, 1st bust, crown reverse, 1797–1800, from

| | £40 | £65 | £135 |

Half guinea, 1787–98, 1800, from

| | £60 | £110 | £225 |

| Guinea, 1787–99, from | £100 | £160 | £400 |

1797. Countermarked Coinage.

Spanish dollars (eight reales) countermarked with the effigy of George III.

Half dollar (2s 5d), oval countermark, from

| | £100 | £200 | £400 |

Half dollar (25d), octagonal countermark, from

| | £150 | £300 | £700 |

Dollar (4s 9d), oval countermark, from

| | £90 | £160 | £300 |

Dollar (4s 9d), octagonal countermark, from

| | £140 | £260 | £450 |

1797–1807. Copper coinage.

Obv: Right-facing laureated bust. Rev: Britannia with olive branch. Des: Heinrich Küchler. Soho Mint, Birmingham.

Farthing, draped bust, 1799

| | £2 | £6 | £30 |

Farthing, short-haired bust, 1806–7

| | £2 | £7 | £30 |

Halfpenny, draped bust, 1799

| | £2 | £6 | £30 |

Halfpenny, short-haired bust, 1806–7

| | £2 | £6 | £30 |

Penny 'Cartwheel', 1797 £15 £30 £125

Penny, short-haired bust, 1806–7

| | £5 | £12 | £55 |

Twopence, 'Cartwheel', 1797

| | £20 | £35 | £160 |

1800–13. Garter coinage.

Obv: Right-facing busts with short hair by Lewis Pingo. Rev: Crown (third guinea) or crowned arms within the Garter.

Third guinea, date below crown, 1801–3

| | £40 | £65 | £140 |

Third guinea, short-hair, 1804–11, from

| | £40 | £65 | £150 |

Half guinea, 6th bust, 1801–3

| | £50 | £90 | £180 |

50

Half guinea, short-hair, 1804–13 from
| | £55 | £95 | £180 |

Guinea, 'military type', 1813
| | £150 | £400 | £850 |

1804–16. Bank of England Tokens.

Struck on Spanish-American dollars (eight reales) and their sub-divisions.
Obv: Right-facing laureated bust of George III. Rev: Britannia seated within a crowned upright oval (dollar) or value within a wreath (other values).

Ninepence, pattern only	—	—	£1000
Eighteen pence, draped bust, 1811–12	£10	£20	£45
Eighteen pence, short hair, 1812–16	£10	£20	£45
Three shillings, draped bust, 1811–12, from	£12	£25	£60
Three shillings, short hair, 1812–16, from	£15	£25	£60
Dollar (5s), 1804, from	£80	£140	£325

1816–20. Sovereign coinage

Obv: Right-facing, short-haired, laureated effigy of George III. Rev: St George and the Dragon (sovereign and crown), crowned shield (half sovereign and half crown to sixpence). Lower denominations (Maundy money) modified from previous designs. Engraved by Benedetto Pistrucci or William Wyon.

From this point coins are priced in VF, EF and Unc grades.

Penny, 1817–18, 1820 from	£10	£15	£20
Twopence, 1817–18, 1829, from	£12	£18	£25
Threepence, 1817–18, 1820, from	£15	£20	£30
Fourpence, 1817–18, 1820, from	£20	£30	£45
Sixpence, 1816–20, from	£12	£35	£65
Shilling, 1816–20, from	£15	£40	£80
Half crown, 'Bull head', 1816–17	£30	£100	£200
Half crown, 'Small head', 1817–20, from	£35	£110	£220
Crown, 1818–20, from	£65	£240	£475
Half sovereign, 1817–20, from	£85	£160	£320
Sovereign, 1817–20, from	£160	£400	£650

Two pounds, pattern only, 1820
— — £14000
Five pounds, pattern only, 1820
— — £50000

George IV (1820–30).

1821–25. First coinage.

Obv: Left-facing laureated effigy. Rev: St George and Dragon (gold and crown), crowned shield (half crown to sixpence), crowned numerals (Maundy money) and helmeted Britannia with trident (copper). Engraved by Benedetto Pistrucci and William Wyon.

Farthing, 1821–23, 1825–26, from	£8	£35	£70
Penny (silver), 1822–30	£8	£12	£20
Twopence, 1822–30	£10	£15	£25
Threepence, small head, 1822	£15	£35	£70
Threepence, large head, 1823–30	£15	£30	£70
Fourpence, 1822–30, from	£20	£25	£40
Sixpence, garnished shield, 1821	£25	£70	£145
Sixpence, shield in garter, 1824–26, from	£25	£75	£110
Shilling, garnished shield, 1821	£25	£85	£150
Shilling, shield in garter, 1823–25, from	£25	£80	£175
Half crown, garnished shield, 1820–23, from	£35	£110	£250
Half crown, shield in garter and collar, 1823–24 from	£40	£125	£260
Crown, St George and Dragon, 1821–22, from	£75	£275	£625
Half sovereign, ornate shield, 1821	£450	£1400	£2250
Half sovereign, plain shield, 1823–25, from	£150	£400	£660
Sovereign, St George and Dragon, 1821–25 from	£170	£450	£850
Two pounds, St George and Dragon, 1823	£400	£750	£1600

1825–30. Second coinage.

Obv: Left-facing, bare-headed profile (William Wyon). Rev: Various crowned shields (Jean Baptiste Merlen) or Britannia (copper coins).

Third farthing (Malta), 1827	£12	£25	£55
Half farthing (Ceylon), 1828, 1830, from	£16	£36	£68
Farthing, 1826–30, from	£8	£35	£75
Halfpenny, 1825–27, from	£25	£65	£120
Penny, 1825–27, from	£30	£80	£230
Sixpence, lion on crown, 1826–29, from	£20	£60	£100
Shilling, lion on crown, 1825–29, from	£12	£30	£70

Half crown, crested shield, 1824–29, from
| | £35 | £95 | £220 |
Crown, proof only, 1826 | — | £1700 | £2000 |
Half sovereign, garnished shield, 1826–28, from
| | £150 | £400 | £600 |
Sovereign, crowned shield, 1825–30, from
| | £150 | £425 | £750 |
Two pounds, mantled shield, proof only
| | — | £2750 | £4000 |
Five pounds, mantled shield, proof only
| | — | £6000 | £10000 |

William IV (1830-37)

Obv: Right-facing, bare-headed profile (William Wyon). Rev: Crowned shield (gold and large silver) or wreathed value (silver penny to shilling).

Third farthing (Malta), 1835
| | £16 | £35 | £65 |
Half farthing (Ceylon), 1837
| | £40 | £95 | £150 |
Farthing, Britannia, 1831, 1834–37, from
| | £12 | £30 | £75 |
Halfpenny, Britannia, 1831, 1834–37
| | £22 | £65 | £125 |

Penny, Britannia, no initials on truncation, 1831, 34, 37
| | £35 | £120 | £250 |
Penny, W.W. on truncation of neck, 1831
| | £40 | £150 | £350 |
Penny (Maundy), 1831–37 £10 | £15 | £20 |
Threehalfpence (colonial issue), 1834–37, from
| | £16 | £30 | £70 |
Twopence (Maundy), 1831–37 from
| | £12 | £18 | £30 |
Threepence (Maundy), 1831–37, from
| | £25 | £30 | £70 |
Threepence (colonial issue), matt surface, 1834–37, from | £25 | £40 | £75 |
Fourpence (Maundy), 1831–37, from
| | £20 | £25 | £40 |
Groat (4d), Britannia, 1836–37
| | £12 | £30 | £50 |
Sixpence, value in wreath, 1831, 1834–37, from
| | £22 | £65 | £120 |
Shilling, value in wreath, 1834–37, from
| | £20 | £70 | £150 |
Half crown, mantled shield, 1834–37, from
| | £45 | £150 | £275 |
Crown, Mantled shield, proof only, 1831
| | — | £2500 | £3250 |
Half sovereign, small size, 1834
| | £150 | £375 | £750 |
Half sovereign, large size, 1835–37, from
| | £70 | £140 | £750 |
Sovereign, 1st bust, 1831–32, from
| | £170 | £460 | £850 |
Sovereign, 2nd bust, 1832–37, from
| | £175 | £450 | £800 |
Two pounds, proof only, 1831
| | — | £3000 | £5000 |

Queen Victoria (1837–1901)

One of the most remarkable aspects of the coinage of this long reign is the longevity of certain coin types. The gold and smaller silver coins remained virtually unchanged until the Diamond Jubilee in 1887 when Her Majesty metamorphosed from teenager to grandmother overnight. William Wyon's Young Head coinage took on a timeless quality, whereas Sir Joseph Edgar Boehm's Jubilee coinage was unpopular and was replaced in 1893 by the Old or Veiled Head coinage designed by Thomas Brock.

There were several major changes in the interim. The sovereign and half sovereign originally used a crowned shield reverse but Pistrucci's St George and Dragon motif was revived in 1871; both designs were in simultaneous use till 1887 when the shield reverse was dropped and St George soldiered on alone, remaining in use to this day, almost two centuries after its debut. Confusion of the armorial half sovereign with the sixpence led to the latter reverting to the wreathed value design in 1887.

Copper was replaced by bronze for the subsidiary coinage in 1860, the so-called Bun effigy by Leonard Charles Wyon being adopted and the Britannia design modified to include Eddystone Lighthouse and a sailing ship, with the date transferred from the obverse to the exergue on the reverse.

The greatest changes occurred in the larger silver coins, including the introduction of the florin or tenth of a pound in 1849, the first step along the long road to decimalisation. There was even a double florin (4 shillings) in the Jubilee series but it was very unpopular and nicknamed the Barmaid's Grief because barmaids allegedly accepted it in error for a crown (5s) and gave drinks or change accordingly.

Apart from a pattern £5 coin in 1839 with a neo-classical motif of Una and the Lion on the reverse, there was no gold coin of higher value than the sovereign until the Golden Jubilee when two and five pound coins were included in the Jubilee series and this set the precedent for the high-value gold coins in the Veiled Head series of 1893.

Branch mints were established at Sydney and Melbourne, and subsequently also at Perth, for the coining of gold mined and refined locally. Such sovereigns and half sovereigns may be identified by the letters S, M or P alongside the date. In 1874–6 and 1881–2 the production of bronze pennies and halfpence was contracted out to the Heaton Mint in Birmingham, and such coins are likewise recognised by the letter H alongside the date.

In view of the fact that the output of the Royal Mint rose to unprecedented levels in the course of this reign it is hardly surprising that there are numerous sub-types and die variants (especially in the sovereigns which provide a life-time study for the specialist collector). This listing is confined to major types. For more detailed coverage of this very complex series see the reading list.

1838–87. Young Head coinage.

Obv: Left-facing profile of Queen Victoria by William Wyon. Rev: Similar to the previous series, but without the Hanoverian shield in the coat of arms.

Quarter farthing (Ceylon), 1839, 1851–53, from			
	£25	£50	£100
Third farthing (Malta), 1844, 66, 68, 76, 78, 81			
1884–5	£24	£30	£50
Half farthing, 1839, 1842–44, from			
	£6	£15	£40
Farthing, 1838–60, from	£7	£30	£45
Halfpenny, 1838–60, from	£8	£20	£50
Penny, 1841–60, from	£10	£40	£75
Penny (Maundy), 1838–87, from			
	£5	£7	£12
Threehalfpence (colonial), 1838–43,			1860
1862, from	£15	£30	£60

Twopence (Maundy), shiny surface, 1838–87,
from   £6   £8   £15
Twopence (colonial), matt surface 1838, 1848,
from   £10   £18   £30
Threepence (Maundy), shiny surface, 1838–87,
from   £15   £30   £60
Threepence (general issue), matt surface,
1838–87, from   £10   £25   £40
Fourpence (Maundy), crowned numeral,
1838–87, from   £7   £10   £15
Groat, Britannia, 1837–49, 1851–55, from
                         £14   £35   £50
Sixpence, 1st head, 1838–66, various dates
from   £22   £50   £110
Sixpence, 2nd head, 1867–80, various dates
from   £20   £45   £80
Sixpence, 3rd head, 1880–87, from
                         £16   £35   £60
Shilling, 1st head, 1838–39
                         £20   £65   £135
Shilling, 2nd head, 1839–46, 1848–67, from
                         £22   £70   £140
Shilling, 3rd head with die number, 1867–79,
from   £18   £45   £90
Shilling, 4th head without die number,
1879–87, from   £15   £45   £75
Half crown, 1839–46, 1848–50, 1874–87, from
                         £35   £85   £150
Crown, 1839, 1844–5, 1847, from
                         £140   £600   £1800
Half sovereign, 1838–85, various dates from
                         £55   £120   £230
Half sovereign, Melbourne, 1873, 1877,
1881–87, from   £110   £350   —
Half sovereign, Sydney, 1871–2, 1875,
1879–87, from   £90   £400   —
Sovereign, shield reverse, 1838–9, 1841–74,
from   £70   £140   £250
Sovereign, shield, Melbourne, 1872–87, from
                         £75   £150   £300
Sovereign, shield, Sydney, 1871–3, 1875–87,
from   £65   £140   £350
Sovereign, St George reverse, 1871–85, various
dates from   £60   £85   £160
Sovereign, St George, Melbourne, 1872–87,
from   £60   £100   £150
Sovereign, St George, Sydney, 1871–87, from
                         £60   £100   £150
Five pounds, Una and the Lion, pattern only
                          —   £16000   £20000

1847–53. Gothic Crown.

Obv: Crowned bust of Queen Victoria by
William Wyon. Rev: Cruciform crowned shields,
with heraldic flowers in the angles, by William
Dyce.
Crown, 1847 (proofs 1847 and 1853)
                         £460   £650   £1450

1849–87. Florin or One Tenth of a Pound.

Obv: Crowned bust of Queen Victoria by
William Wyon. Rev: As crown, by William Dyce.
Florin, 'Godless' (D.G. omitted), 1849
                         £30   £75   £145
Florin, Gothic lettering, date in Roman numer-
als, 1851–87   £35   £100   £170

1860–95. Bronze Young Head Coinage.

Obv: 'Bun' bust of Queen Victoria. Rev: Helmeted Britannia with trident, Eddystone Lighthouse (left) and sailing ship (right), with date in exergue. Engraved by Leonard Charles Wyon.

Farthing, 1860–95, various dates from
£3 £18 £30

Farthing, Heaton, 1874–76, 1881–82, from
£4 £20 £35

Halfpenny, 1860–94, various dates from
£8 £25 £50

Halfpenny, Heaton, 1874–76, 1881–82, from
£10 £30 £70

Penny, 1860–94, various dates from
£12 £35 £65

Penny, Heaton, 1874–76, 1881–82, from
£12 £35 £65

1887–93. Jubilee Coinage.

Obv: Crowned bust of Queen Victoria by Si Joseph Edgar Boehm. Rev: St George and Dragon (gold and crown) by Benedetto Pistrucci, crowned shields and crossed sceptres (double florin, florin), crowned shield (sixpence and shilling), Britannia (groat) or crowned numeral (threepence).

Penny (Maundy), 1888–92, from
£3 £7 £12

Twopence (Maundy) £4 £8 £14

Threepence (Maundy), shiny surface, 1888–92 from £10 £20 £40

Threepence, matt surface, 1887–92, from
£3 £9 £18

Fourpence (Maundy), 1887–92, from
£4 £9 £10

Groat, 1888 £12 £35 60

Sixpence, shield reverse, 1887
£5 £10 £20

Sixpence, wreath reverse, 1887–93, from
£7 £25 £40

Shilling, small bust, 1887–89, from
£5 £10 £20

Shilling, large bust, 1889–92, from
£8 £30 £60

Florin, 1887–92, from £8 £16 £30

Half crown, 1887–92, from £10 £15 £40

Double florin, 1887–90, from
£20 £40 £65

Crown, 1887–92, from £22 £40 £70

Half sovereign, 1887–93, from
£40 £60 £80

Half sovereign, Melbourne, 1887, 1893, from
£90 £250 £450
Half sovereign, Sydney, 1887, 1889, 1891, from
£90 £220 £400
Sovereign, 1887–92, from £50 £70 £90
Sovereign, Melbourne, 1887–93, from
£55 £100 £120
Sovereign, Sydney, 1887–93, from
£75 £100 £130
Two pounds, 1887, 1893, from
£240 £375 £480
Two pounds, Sydney, 1887
— — —
Five pounds, 1887, 1893, from
£450 £650 £1300
Five pounds, Sydney, 1887
— — —

1893–1901. Veiled Head Coinage.

Obv: Bust of Queen Victoria by Thomas Brock.
Rev: as for previous issues.
Farthing, bright finish, 1895–97, from
£2 £12 £18
Farthing, dark finish, 1897–1901, from
£2 £7 £12
Halfpenny, 1895–1901, from
£2 £6 £15
Penny, 1895–1901, from £2 £7 £15
Penny (Maundy), 1893–1901
£3 £6 £12
Twopence (Maundy), 1893–1901
£4 £7 £15
Threepence (Maundy), shiny surface, 1893–1901 £5 £15 £20
Threepence, matt surface, 1893–1901, from
£3 £14 £20
Fourpence (Maundy), 1893–1901
£6 £8 £15
Sixpence, 1893–1901, from £8 £18 £35
Shilling, 1893–1901, from £7 £20 £40
Florin, 1893–1901, from £16 £40 £65
Half crown, 1893–1901, from
£15 £40 £65
Crown, 1893–1901, from £32 £70 £150
Half sovereign, 1893–1901, from
£40 £55 £90

Half sovereign, Melbourne, 1893, 1896, 1899, 1900, from £90 £300 —
Half sovereign, Perth, 1899–1900, from
£250 — —
Half sovereign, Sydney, 1893, 1897, 1900, from
£90 £300 —
Sovereign, 1893–1901, from
£50 £65 £85
Sovereign, Melbourne, 1893–1901, from
£60 £90 £100
Sovereign, Perth, 1899–1901, from
£75 £90 £130
Sovereign, Sydney, 1893–1901, from
£60 £75 £100
Two pounds, 1893 £325 £500 £650
Five pounds, 1893 £600 £820 £1200

Edward VII (1901–10)

Apart from the profile, the only major change in this series was the standing figure of Britannia (florin) in the finest Art Nouveau idiom. A branch mint was opened at Ottawa for the refining and coining of Canadian gold and coins were indicated by the letter C beside the date.

Obv: Right-facing profile by George William de Saulles from the effigy by Emil Fuchs. Rev: St

George and Dragon (gold and crown), crowned shield (half crown), standing Britannia (florin), lion on crown (shilling), wreathed value (sixpence), wreathed numerals (Maundy series), Britannia (bronze).

Farthing, 1902–10, from	£1	£7	£14
Halfpenny, 1902–10, from	£4	£8	£25
Penny, 1902–10, from	£2	£14	£22
Penny (Maundy), 1902–10, from			
	£5	£7	£10
Twopence (Maundy), 1902–10, from			
	£5	£7	£12
Threepence (Maundy), shiny surface, 1902–10, from			
	£8	£12	£30
Threepence (circulating), matt surface, 1902–10, from			
	£3	£7	£15
Fourpence (Maundy), 1902–10, from			
	£6	£8	£12
Sixpence, 1902–10, from	£4	£18	£32
Shilling, 1902–10, from	£5	£15	£35
Florin, 1902–10, from	£14	£35	£65
Half crown, 1902–10, from			
	£18	£50	£70
Crown, 1902	£45	£85	£125
Half sovereign, 1902–10, from			
	£40	£45	£55
Half sovereign, Melbourne, 1906–9, from			
	£40	£80	£170
Half sovereign, Perth, 1904, 1908–9, from			
	£130	£350	—
Half sovereign, Sydney, 1902–3, 1906, 1908, 1910, from	£45	£100	£175
Sovereign, 1902–10, from	£45	£60	£75
Sovereign, C (Ottawa), 1908–10, from			
	£80	£220	—
Sovereign, Melbourne, 1902–10, from			
	£60	£80	£120
Sovereign, Perth, 1902–10, from			
	£60	£80	£120
Sovereign, Sydney, 1902–10, from			
	£60	£80	£120
Two pounds, 1902	£180	£280	£360
Five pounds, 1902	£400	£550	£750

George V (1910–36)

This reign was dominated by the First World War (1914-18) and the industrial and political upheavals of the Twenties and the Depression, all of which had their impact on the coinage. Gold was withdrawn from circulation in August 1914 and replaced by paper money, but sovereign and half sovereigns continued to be struck, mainly for overseas bullion shipment, and further branch mints were opened at Bombay and Pretoria whose gold coins are identified by the letters I (India) and SA (South Africa).

Production of halfpence and pennies was subcontracted to the Heaton and King's Norton mints in Birmingham, and denoted by the initials H or KN beside the date. The coins are grouped in several series, according to the king's effigy which was modified in 1926 and then reduced in 1927 in conjunction with new reverse designs. During the period of the first (Large Head) coinage silver was debased from sterling (.925 fine) to .500 fine in 1920. This reign also witnessed Britain's first commemorative coin, the crown of 1935 celebrating the King's Silver Jubilee.

1911–26. Large Head Coinage.

58

Obv: Left-facing profile by Sir Bertram Mackennal. Rev: as previous types. Sculptor's initials with stops (B.M.).

Third farthing (Malta), 1913	£7	£20	£30
Farthing, dark finish, 1911–18, from			
	50p	£4	£10
Farthing, bright finish, 1918–25, from			
	50p	£3	£8
Halfpenny, 1911–25, from	£1	£5	£9
Penny, 1911–22, 1926, from	£3	£12	£35
Penny, Heaton, 1912, 1918–19, from			
	£3	£25	£70
Penny, Kings Norton, 1918–19, from			
	£50	£260	£800
Penny (Maundy), 1911–20, .925 silver, from			
	£5	£8	£15
Penny (Maundy), 1921–27, .500 silver, from			
	£4	£7	£12
Twopence (Maundy), 1911–20, .925 silver			
	£5	£8	£15
Twopence (Maundy), 1921–27, .500 silver			
	£5	£8	£14
Threepence (Maundy), shiny surface, 1911–20, .925 silver			
	£6	£12	£25
Threepence (Maundy), shiny surface, 1921–27, .500 silver			
	£5	£10	£20
Threepence, matt surface, 1911–20, .925 silver, from			
	£2	£4	£8
Threepence, matt surface, 1920–26, .500 silver, from			
	£2	£3	£8
Fourpence (Maundy), 1911–20, .925 silver			
	£5	£10	£15
Sixpence, 1911–20, .925 silver, from			
	£2	£10	£25
Sixpence, 1920–26, .500 silver, from			
	£2	£10	£22
Shilling, 1911–19, .925 silver, from			
	£4	£16	£32
Shilling, 1920–26, .500 silver, from			
	£2	£15	£35
Florin, 1911–19, .925 silver, from			
	£8	£22	£40
Florin, 1920–26, .500 silver, from			
	£10	£25	£40
Half crown, 1911–19, .925 silver, from			
	£8	£18	£35
Half crown, 1920–26, .500 silver, from			
	£7	£15	£30
Half sovereign, 1911–15, from			
	£40	£60	£80
Half sovereign, Melbourne, 1915			
	£40	£70	£120
Half sovereign, Perth, 1911, 1915, 1918, from			
	£35	£70	£100
Half sovereign, Sydney, 1911–12, 1914–16, from			
	£40	£70	£110
Half sovereign, South Africa, 1925–2			
	£40	£65	£100
Sovereign, 1911–17, 1925, from			
	£35	£60	£70
Sovereign, Canada, 1911, 1913–14, 1916–19, from			
	£100	£120	£150
Sovereign, India, 1918	£40	£75	—
Sovereign, Melbourne, 1911–26, from			
	£35	£75	£100
Sovereign, Perth, 1911–26, from			
	£35	£75	£100
Sovereign, Sydney, 1911–26, from			
	£35	£70	£90
Sovereign, South Africa, 1923–26, from			
	£60	£80	£95
Two pounds, proof only, 1911			
	—	—	£675
Five pounds, proof only, 1911			
	—	—	£1500

1925–27. Modified Coinage.

Obv: Effigy with finer detail, beading more pronounced and sculptor's initials BM (without stops) closer to the back of the neck. Rev: As before.

Farthing, 1926–36, from	50p	£3	£6
Halfpenny, 1925–27, from	£2	£10	£30
Penny, 1926–27, from	£2	£8	£25
Threepence, 1926	£3	£7	£18
Sixpence, 1926–27, from	£2	£8	£25
Shilling, 1926–27	£3	£18	£30
Half crown, 1926–27, from	£8	£25	£40

1927–36. Small Head Coinage.

Obv: Narrower effigy. BM without stops on truncation. Rev: New motifs on silver coins (threepence to crown) by Kruger Gray; Maundy money and bronze unchanged.

Farthing, 1926–36, from	50p	£4	£6
Halfpenny, 1928–36, from	£1	£5	£8
Penny, 1928–36, from	£2	£8	£30
Penny (Maundy), 1928–36	£6	£10	£18
Twopence (Maundy), 1928–36			
	£6	£10	£18
Threepence (Maundy), 1928–36			
	£15	£25	£50
Threepence (three acorns), 1828–36, from			
	£2	£5	£8
Fourpence (Maundy), 1928–36, from			
	£6	£10	£15
Sixpence (six acorns), 1928–30, from			
	£1	£5	£10
Shilling (lion on crown), 1927–36, from			
	£2	£4	£10

Florin (four shields and crowned sceptres), 1928–36, from £4 £9 £16
Half crown (waisted shield), 1928–36, from £5 £10 £18
Crown (crown in wreath of heraldic flowers), 1928–36 from £55 £85 £130

1935. Silver Jubilee of King George V.

Obv: Effigy by Sir Bertram Mackennal. Rev: St George and the Dragon by Percy Metcalfe.
Crown £12 £16 £28

Edward VIII (1936)

Edward VIII came to the throne in January 1936 but abdicated eleven months later. The Royal Mint had prepared obverse and reverse designs for a full series from the bronze farthing to the gold five pounds. Apart from the patterns held by the Mint, a few examples have leaked on to the market, notably the brass threepence, but all are extremely rare.

1937. Pattern Coinage.

Obv: Left-facing profile by Humphrey Paget. Rev: Various new types by Percy Metcalfe (brass threepence), Humphrey Paget (half-penny), Wilson Parker (farthing) or Kruger Gray (silver coins).

Farthing (wren), 1937   —   —   —
Halfpenny (*Golden Hind*), 1937
   —   —   —
Penny (Britannia), 1937   —   —   —
Threepence (three interlocking rings)
   —   —   —
Sixpence (six interlocking rings)
   —   —   —
Shilling (Scottish lion squatting on crown)
   —   —   —
Florin (crowned Tudor rose flanked by thistle and shamrock)   —   —
Half crown (heraldic flag) —   —   —
Crown / crowned shield with supporters)
   —   —   —

Sovereign (St George and Dragon)
   —   —   —
Two pounds (St George and Dragon)
   —   —   —
Five pounds (St George and Dragon)
   —   —   —

King George VI (1936–52)

The only gold coins of this reign were those in the Coronation proof set of 1937. The coinage was chiefly remarkable for two different three-pences in simultaneous use, the tiny silver coin continuing till 1944 alongside the brass twelve-sided coin, and two different shillings. Although it is widely believed that the Scottish shilling was intended as a compliment to Queen Elizabeth, it had been decided to issue such a coin in the Edward VIII series, to silence protests from the Scots over the shilling of 1927–36 which was regarded as a specifically English design. To repay the bullion lent by the USA for the war effort, the silver coinage was called in and replaced by coins struck in cupro-nickel from 1947 onwards. The other major change was in the omission of the title IND. IMP. (Emperor of India) after the Indian sub-continent gained independence in 1947. The Maundy coins were originally struck in .500 fine silver but when the silver coins were debased to cupro-nickel, sterling (.925 fine) silver was restored to the Maundy series.

1937–46. First coinage.

Obv: Left-facing profile by Humphrey Paget.
Rev: Various motifs by Wilson Parker (farthing),
Humphrey Paget (halfpenny), Percy Metcalfe
(brass threepence), Kruger Gray (silver) and
Benedetto Pistrucci (gold).

	EF	Unc
Farthing, (wren), 1937–48, from	50p	£1
Halfpenny (*Golden Hinde*), 1937–48, from		
	£1	£2
Penny (Britannia), 1937–40, 1944–48, from		
	£1	£3
Penny (Maundy), 1937–46, from	£10	£17
Twopence (Maundy), 1937–46, from	£8	£12
Threepence (Maundy), 1937–46, from		
	£12	£30
Threepence (shield on rose), 1937–45, from		
	£1	£3
Threepence (thrift), 1937–48, from	£1	£3
Fourpence (Maundy), 1937–46, from		
	£10	£17
Sixpence (crown over GRI), 1937–46	£1	£3
Shilling (English: lion standing on crown), 1937–46, from		
	£2	£5
Shilling (Scottish: lion squatting on crown), 1937-46, from		
	£2	£5
Florin (crowned rose), 1937–46, from		
	£3	£5
Half crown (tilting shield), 1937–46, from		
	£3	£6
Crown (shield and supporters), 1937		
	£20	£30

Half sovereign, proof only, 1937	—	£160
Sovereign, proof only, 1937	£270	£350
Two pounds, proof only, 1937	—	£375
Five pounds, proof only, 1937	—	£750

1947–48. Second coinage.

As above but cupro-nickel instead of .500 silver
in the circulating coins, and .925 silver instead
of .500 silver in the Maundy coins.

Penny, 1947–48	£10	£18
Twopence, 1947–48	£10	£16
Threepence, 1947–48	£15	£30
Fourpence, 1947–48	£11	£17
Sixpence, 1947–48	£1	£3
Shilling, (English), 1947–48	£1	£3
Shilling, (Scottish), 1947–48	£1	£3
Florin, 1947–48	£1	£3
Half crown, 1947–48	£2	£4

1949–52. Third coinage.

As previous types, but IND,IMP. Omitted from
the king's titles on the obverse.
New reverse for sixpence (crown over cursive
GR).

Farthing, 1949–52, from	£1	£3
Halfpenny, 1949–52, from	£1	£2
Penny, 1949–51, from	£1	£3
Penny (Maundy), 1949–52	£11	£20
Twopence (Maundy), 1949–52	£10	£20
Threepence (Maundy), 1949–52	£15	£35
Threepence (thrift), 1949–52, from	£1	£5
Fourpence (Maundy), 1949–52	£20	£40
Sixpence, 1949–52, from	£1	£3
Shilling (English), 1949–52, from	£2	£4
Shilling (Scottish), 1949–52, from	£2	£4
Florin, 1949–51, from	£2	£8
Half crown, 1949–51, from	£3	£6

1951. Festival of Britain.

Obv: Profile of King George VI by Humphrey Paget. Rev: St George and the Dragon by Benedetto Pistrucci. Incuse inscription on edge: MDCCCLI CIVIUM INDUSTRIA FLORET CIVITAS MCMLI.

Crown, 1951	£6	£8

Queen Elizabeth II (1952–)

The third longest reign in British history (after Queen Victoria and King George III), it has witnessed the most dramatic changes in the coinage since 1816, notably the replacement of the £sd system inherited from the Romans and the introduction of the decimal £p system in 1968–71. This coincided with the transfer of the Royal Mint from Tower Hill, London to new premises at Llantrisant, South Wales. The minting of separate English and Scottish shillings continued till 1968.

Unlike the coinage of Queen Victoria, changes have been made in the portraits of Queen Elizabeth over the years. The laureated bust by Mary Gillick was used for the £sd coinage, followed by the bust by Arnold Machin for the decimal coins of 1968–84, then the crowned profile by Raphael Maklouf (1985–97) and the profile by Ian Rank-Broadley since 1998. The word NEW was dropped from the reverse in 1982.

Inflation over the past half century has resulted in the withdrawal of the farthing (1956) and the new halfpenny (1984), the reduction in the sizes of several coins (1990–97) and the introduction of new denominations, beginning with the 20p (1982). The replacement of paper money by coins began with the 50 new pence in 1969 and has continued with the introduction of brass £1 and £2 coins, in 1983 and 1986 respectively. Bi-metallic £2 coins were adopted in 1998. A novel feature of the pound coins has been the use of a different reverse motif each year.

In the pre-decimal period crowns (5 shillings) were issued in Coronation year and 1960, followed by a coin in memory of Sir Winston Churchill (1965). In the decimal system commemorative crowns were originally valued at 25 new pence, but since 1989 they have been more sensibly tariffed at £5. In addition, commemorative 50p and £2 coins have been released on a number of occasions.

1953. First Coinage.

Obv: Right-facing laureated bust by Mary Gillick, with BRITT OMN in title. Rev: New types for cupro-nickel coins and brass threepence (William Gardner, Edgar Fuller and Cecil Thomas).

Farthing (wren)	50p	£1
Halfpenny (*Golden Hinde*)	50p	£1
Penny (Britannia)	75p	£1
Penny (Maundy)	£60	£100
Twopence (Maundy)	£40	£60
Threepence (Maundy)	£55	£80
Threepence (portcullis)	50p	£1
Fourpence (Maundy)	£50	£75
Sixpence (flowers)	£1	£2
Shilling (English)	50p	£1
Shilling (Scottish)	50p	£1
Florin (flowers)	£1	£2
Half crown (crowned shield)	£1	£3
Crown (Queen on horseback)	£3	£8

1954. Second coinage.

As above, but BRITT OMN omitted from obverse legend. Note: the designs and specifications of the Maundy coins have remained unchanged to the present day.

Farthing, 1954–56	£1	£2
Halfpenny, 1954–67, from	—	£1
Penny 1954–67, from	—	50p
Penny (Maundy)	£10	£16
Twopence (Maundy)	£12	£17
Threepence (Maundy)	£15	£30
Threepence (portcullis)	—	£1
Fourpence (Maundy)	£13	£18
Sixpence, 1954–67, from	—	£1
Shilling (English), 1954–66, from	—	£1
Shilling (Scottish), 1954–66, from	—	£1
Florin, 1954–67, from	£1	£1.50
Half crown, 1954–67, from	—	£1
Crown, 1960	£3	£6
Sovereign, 1957–59, 1962–68, from		
	£45	£60

1965. In Memory of Sir Winston Churchill.

Obv: Bust by Mary Gillick. Rev: Portrait of Churchill by Oscar Nemon.
Crown, various versions from   £1   £2

DECIMAL COINAGE

Beginning in 1971 the Royal Mint began producing proof sets each year (see section listing proof and specimen sets). Many of the decimal proof sets have been broken up and as a result we price these coins individually. The circulating coins have been minted in such vast numbers that only those in Uncirculated condition are considered worth collecting and accordingly prices quoted for coins in this section are in Uncirculated and proof condition only. In the same period the Royal Mint has also produced off-metal editions (i.e. gold or silver versions of coins normally issued in base alloys) as well as piedforts (coins of double weight and thickness). These are outside the scope of this catalogue.

1968–82. First Coinage.

Obv: bust by Arnold Machin. Inscribed NEW PENCE. Rev: Various heraldic motifs by Christopher Ironside.

	Unc.	Proof
½p (crown), 1971–84, from	25p	£1
1p (portcullis), 1971–82, from	30p	£1
2p (plumes), 1971–82, from	60p	£2
5p (crowned thistle), 1968–82, from	75p	£5
10p (crowned lion), 1968–82, from	£1	£3
50p (Britannia), 1969–82, from	£3	£5

1972. Royal Silver Wedding.

Obv: Machin bust. Rev: crown over EP surrounded by flowers.

25p	£3.50	£12

1973. British Entry into the European Common Market.

Obv: Machin bust. Rev: nine hands clasped in a circle by David Wynne.

50p	£3	£5

1977. Silver Jubilee.

Obv: Queen on horseback. Rev: Coronation regalia in floral border.

25p	£3.50	£12

1980. 80th Birthday of Queen Elizabeth, the Queen Mother.

Obv: Machin bust. Rev: Queen Mother surrounded by bows and lions.

25p	£3	£10

1981. Royal Wedding.

Obv: Machin bust. Rev: Conjoined profiles of Charles and Diana.

25p	£3	£1⬤

1982–84. Second Coinage.

Modified reverse and word NEW omitted. 20⬤ (crowned rose) by William Gardner.

½p	50p	£⬤
1p	50p	£2.5⬤
2p	£2	£2.5⬤
5p	£3.50	£⬤
10p	£4	£⬤
20p	£3	£⬤
50p	£4	£⬤
£1 Royal Arms (1983)	£5	£⬤
£1 Scottish Thistle (1984)	£5	£⬤

1985–97. Third Coinage.

)bv: crowned profile by Raphael Maklouf. Rev:
As previous types.

p	25p	£1
2p	40p	£1
5p (24mm)	£2.50	£4
5p (18mm, 1990)	£1	£2
10p (28.5mm)	£3	£4
10p (24.5mm, 1992)	£2	£4
20p	£1	£3
50p (30mm)	£3	£5
50p (27mm, 1997)	£4	£7
£1 Welsh Leek (1985, 1990)	£5	£8
£1 Irish Flax (1986, 1991)	£5	£8
£1 English Oak (1987, 1992)	£5	£8
£1 Royal Shield (1988)	£5	£8
£1 Scottish Thistle (1989)	£5	£8
£1 Royal Arms (1993)	£5	£8
£1 Scottish Lion (1994)	£5	£8
£1 Welsh Dragon (1995)	£5	£8
£1 Celtic Cross (1996)	£5	£8
£1 English Lions (1997)	£5	£8
Half sovereign, 1985–88, 1990–97, proof only from	—	70
Sovereign, 1985–88, 1990–97, proof only from	—	£100

Two pounds, 1985, 1987–88, 1990–93, proofs from	—	£250
Five pounds, 1985, 1987–88, 1990-7, from	£550	£600

1986. Commonwealth Games, Edinburgh.

Obv: Maklouf profile. Rev: Scottish thistle and saltire cross.

£2	£4	£7

1989. Tercentenary of the Bill of Rights.
Obv: Maklouf profile. Rev: crown, mace and entwined W and M.

£2	£4	£8

1989. Tercentenary of the Claim of Right.

Obv: Maklouf profile. Rev: Scottish crown, mace and entwined W and M.

£2	£4	£8

1989. Quincentenary of the Sovereign.

Obv: Queen on throne, after the style of the Tudor sovereign. Rev: crowned arms on Tudor rose.

Half sovereign, proof only	—	£90
Sovereign, proof only	—	£170
Two pounds, proof only	—	£320
Five pounds	£550	£600

1990. 90th Birthday of the Queen Mother.

1993. 40th Anniversary of the Coronation.

Obv: Maklouf profile. Rev: crown and entwined Ss flanked by thistle and rose.

£5   £8   £12

1992–3. Completion of Single Market and Britain's Presidency of EC.

Obv: Maklouf profile. Rev: stars, conference table and seats (Mary Milner-Dickens).

50p   £4   £8

Obv: Gillick profile surrounded by trumpeters, swords and sceptres. Rev: Imperial Crown surrounded by trumpets.

£5   £8   £12

1994. 50th Anniversary of D-Day.

Obv: Maklouf profile. Rev: Ships and planes invading Normandy.

50p   £4   £8

1994. Tercentenary of the Bank of England.

Obv: Maklouf profile. Rev: Crowned WM cipher over the Bank emblem.

£2 £4 £8

1995. 25th Anniversary of Admission to the European Union.

Obv: Maklouf profile. Rev: Twelve stars.

50p £3 £7

1995. 50th Anniversary of the End of World War II.

Obv: Maklouf profile. Rev: Dove of peace (Norman Sill).

£2 £4 £7

1995. 50th Anniversary of the United Nations.

Obv: Maklouf profile. Rev: Flags radiating from UN emblem.

£2 £5 £7

1996. Euro 96 Football Championship.

Scyphate. Obv: Maklouf profile. Rev: stylised football.

£2 £5 £9

1996. 70th Birthday of Queen Elizabeth.
Obv: Maklouf profile in a beaded circle. Rev: Windsor Castle and flags.

£5 £8 £12

1997. Technological Progress.
Bi-metallic coin. Obv: Maklouf profile within a beaded circle. Rev: four concentric circles symbolising progress from the Iron Age to Internet (Bruce Rushin).

£2 £5 £7

1997. Royal Golden Wedding.

Obv: Conjoined busts of the Queen and Duke of Edinburgh. Rev: crown, anchor and shields of the Queen and Duke.

£5   £8   £12

1998. Third Coinage.

Obv: Profile by Ian Rank-Broadley. Rev: As previous types.

1p	50p	£
2p	£1	£3.5
5p	£1	£
10p	£2	£
20p	£2	£
50p	£2.50	£
£1 Royal Arms (1998)	£6	£
£1 Scottish Lion (1999)	£5	£
£1 Welsh Dragon (2000)	£4	£
£1 Celtic Cross (2001)	£4	£
£1 English Lions (2002)	£5	£
£2 Technological progress (as 1997)		
	£5	£
Half sovereign	—	£7
Sovereign	—	£14
Two pounds	—	£28
Five pounds	£550	£60

1998. 50th Anniversary of the National Health Service.

Obv: Rank-Broadley profile. Rev: Light radiating from cupped hands (David Cornell).

50p   £3   £

1998. 50th Birthday of the Prince of Wales.

Obv: Rank-Broadley profile. Rev: Prince Charles.
£5 £8 £12

1999. Rugby World Cup.
Obv: Rank-Broadley profile. Rev: Rugby ball and goal-posts.
£2 £5 £8

1999. In Memory of Diana, Princess of Wales.
Obv: Rank-Broadley profile. Rev: Diana, Princess of Wales and dates 1961–1997 (David Cornell).
£5 £8 £12

2000. Millennium.
Obv: Rank-Broadley profile. Rev: Clock-face approaching midnight and map of the British Isles.
£5 £8 £12

2000. Hundredth Birthday of the Queen Mother.
Obv: Rank-Broadley profile. Rev: profile and signature of the Queen Mother.
£5 £8 £12

2000. 150th Anniversary of Public Libraries.
Obv: Rank-Broadley profile. Rev: library façade and open book.
50p £4 £7

2001. Centenary of the Victorian Era.
Obv: Rank-Broadley profile. Rev: Wyon profile of Queen Victoria and arches.
£5 £8 £12

2001. Radio Centenary.
Obv: Rank-Broadley profile. Rev: symbolic of Marconi's experiments.
£2 £5 £8

2002. Tribute to the Late Queen Mother.
Obv: Rank-Broadley profile. Rev: Queen Elizabeth the Queen Mother.
£5 £8 £12

2002. Golden Jubilee.
Obv: Equestrian portrait. Rev: Her Majesty in the Robes of State.
£5 £8 £12

2002. Golden Jubilee.
Obv: Rank-Broadley profile. Rev: Crowned shield within a wreath (after Merlen).

Half sovereign	£40	£75
Sovereign	£75	£150
Five pounds	£480	£600

2002. Commonwealth Games.
Obv: Rank-Broadley profile. Rev: tracks with national emblems inset.

£2 (England)	£5	£7
£2 (Scotland)	£5	£7
£2 (Wales)	£5	£7
£2 (Northern Ireland)	£5	£7

2003. 50th Anniversary of the Coronation.
Obv: Stylised profile of the Queen. Rev: GOD SAVE THE QUEEN.
£5 £7 £10

2003. Centenary of the WSPU (Women's Suffrage Movement).
Obv: Rank-Broadley profile. Rev: Suffragette, banner and ballot paper Mary Milner Dickens).
50p £4 £7

2003. 50th Anniversary of DNA.

Obv: Rank-Broadley profile. Rev: DNA double helix.

£2   £5   £7

2004. Bicentenary of Steam Locomotion.

Obv: Rank-Broadley profile. Rev: Penydarren locomotive of Richard Trevithick, 1804

£2   £5   £7

BRITANNIA COINAGE

In 1987 the Royal Mint launched a series of four gold bullion coins as a rival to the universally popular Krugerrand series from South Africa. Known as the Britannia coins, from their reverse motif, they have been struck in 22 carat gold but respectively containing a tenth, quarter, half and one ounce troy of pure gold and denominated £10, £25, £50 and £100. The original reverse showed the standing figure of Britannia, inspired by De Saulles' reverse for the florin of 1902. A new reverse, showing Britannia in a chariot drawn by two horses, was adopted in 1997. In the same year the Mint also began producing silver bullion coins containing tenth, quarter, half and one ounce of pure silver and respectively denominated 20p, 50p, £1 and £2. These originally used the standing Britannia reverse but switched to the chariot motif in 1998 and then reverted to the standing Britannia in 1999. The denomination appears on the obverse below the Queen's effigy, while the reverse bears an inscription signifying the weight of the precious metal.

1987–96. First Coinage.

Obv: Maklouf profile. Rev: Standing Britannia with trident and shield.

	Unc.	Proof
£10, from	£15	£70
£25, from	£35	£100
£50, from	£70	£180
£100, from	£180	£350

1997. Second Coinage.

Obv: Maklouf profile. Rev: Britannia in chariot.

20p	£6	£12
50p	£8	£18

£1	£10	£20
£2	£15	£30
£10	£18	£70
£25	£40	£130
£50	£80	£250
£100	£200	£440

1998. Third Coinage.

Obv: Rank-Broadley profile. Rev: Standing Britannia with trident and shield.

20p	£6	£12
50p	£8	£15
£1	£10	£20
£2	£15	£30
£10	£18	£70
£25	£40	£130
£50	£80	£250
£100	£200	£440

2003. Fourth Coinage.

Obv: Rank-Broadley profile. Rev: Helmeted profile of Britannia by Philip Nathan.

£2	£15	—

[other coins in this series will probably be released later].

PROOF AND SPECIMEN SETS

Proofs were originally struck on specially polished blanks to ensure that the dies were perfect but out of this arose the custom of making up sets of such coins for presentation purposes. This practice goes back to 1746 when the Mint produced a wedge-shaped case containing the silver sixpence, shilling, half crown and crown struck to proof standard. It is not known how many cases were produced but the edition must have been quite limited. This custom was rarely employed in the 19th century, but proof sets accompanied the introduction of the Jubilee and Veiled Head coins of Queen Victoria in 1887 and 1893 respectively, and then became a regular feature at Coronations from 1902 onwards. The present system of producing cased sets of proofs and specimen folders, including precious metal versions and piedforts (double thickness coins) developed from 1970 onwards.

George II
1746 Sixpence – crown (4 coins) £11000

George IV
1826 Farthing – five pounds (11 coins) £20000

William IV
1831 Coronation, farthing – two pounds (14 coins) £17000

Victoria
1839 Farthing – Una and Lion £5 (15 coins) £30000
1853 Quarter farthing – sovereign (16 coins) £27000
1877 Bronze farthing – penny (3 coins) £2500
1887 Golden Jubilee, threepence – five pounds (11 coins) £6000
1893 Veiled Head, threepence – five pounds (10 coins) £6500
1893 Veiled Head, threepence – crown (6 coins) £1300

Edward II
1902 Coronation, Maundy penny – £5 matt proofs (13 coins) £1600
1902 Coronation, Maundy penny – sovereign matt proofs (11) £575

George V

1911 Coronation, Maundy penny – five
pounds (12 coins)   £2500
1911 Coronation, Maundy penny – sovereign
(10 coins)   £875
1911 Coronation, Maundy penny – half crown
(8 coins)   £430
1927 Threepence – crown (6 coins)   £235

George VI

1937 Coronation, Half sovereign – five
pounds (4 coins)   £1600
1937 Coronation, Farthing – crown (15 coins)
  £175
1950 Mid-century, Farthing – half crown
(9 coins)   £70
1951 Festival of Britain, Farthing – crown
(10 coins)   £85

Elizabeth II

1953 Coronation, Farthing – crown (10 coins)
  £50
1953 Coronation, Farthing – half crown
(9 coins plastic wallet)   £14
1968 Decimal, Halfpenny – 10 new pence
(5 coins plastic wallet)   £3
1970 Last £sd coins, Halfpenny – half crown
(8 coins)   £20
1971 Proof set, Halfpenny – 50p (6 coins) £12
1972 Proof set, ½p – 50p and Silver Wedding
crown (7 coins)   £16
1973 Proof set, ½p – 50p (6 coins)   £14
1974 Proof set ½p – 50p (6 coins)   £15
1975 Proof set ½p – 50p (6 coins)   £16
1976 Proof set ½p – 50p (six coins)   £16
1977 Proof set ½p – 50p and Silver Jubilee
crown (7 coins)   £16
1978 Proof set ½p – 50p (6 coins)   £15
1979 Proof set ½p – 50p (6 coins)   £15
1980 Proof set ½p – 50p (6 coins)   £14
1980 Proof set half sovereign – £5 (4 coins)
  £760
1981 Proof set ½p – 50p (6 coins)   £16
1981 Proof set ½p – gold £5, Silver Wedding
crown (9 coins)   £680
1982 Proof set half sovereign – £5 (4 coins)
  £750
1982 Proof set ½p – 50p (7 coins)   £16
1982 Uncirculated specimen set ½p – 50p
(7 coins)   £10
1983 Proof set half sovereign – £2 (3 coins)
  £350
1983 Proof set ½p – £1 (8 coins)   £20

1983 Uncirculated specimen set ½p – £1
(8 coins)   £16
1984 Proof set half sovereign – £5 (3 coins)
  £600
1984 Proof set ½p – Scottish £1 (8 coins) £18
1984 Uncirculated specimen set (8 coins) £15
1985 Proof set half sovereign – £5 Maklouf
effigy (4 coins)   £775
1985 Proof de luxe set 1p – Welsh £1 (7 coins)
  £25
1985 Proof set 1p – Welsh £1 (7 coins)   £18
1985 Uncirculated specimen set (7 coins) £15
1986 Proof set half sovereign – £2
Commonwealth Games   £420
1986 Proof de luxe set 1p – NI £1, £2 Games
(8 coins)   £24
1986 As above but ordinary proof set   £22
1986 Uncirculated specimen set (8 coins) £15
1987 Proof Britannia set (4 coins)   £750
1987 Proof Britannia, 1/10oz, 1/4oz (2 coins)
  £150
1987 Proof set half sovereign – £2 (3 coins)
  £360
1987 Proof de luxe set 1p – English £1
(7 coins)   £27
1987 As above but ordinary case (7 coins) £18
1987 Uncirculated specimen set (7 coins) £10
1988 Proof Britannia set (4 coins)   £750
1988 Proof Britannia, 1/10oz, 1/4oz (2 coins)
  £150
1988 Proof set half sovereign – £2 (3 coins)
  £325
1988 De luxe proof set 1p – Royal Arms £1
(7 coins)   £30
1988 Standard proof set (7 coins)   £25
1988 Uncirculated specimen set (7 coins) £12
1989 Britannia proof set (94 coins)   £760
1989 Britannia set 1/10 oz, ½ oz (2 coins) £150
1989 500th anniversary sovereign set
(4 coins)   £950
1989 As above, but half sovereign – £2
(3 coins)   £450
1989 Proof set, Bill and Claim of Rights
(2 coins)   £40
1989 As above but piedfort proof set
(2 coins)   £85
1989 Uncirculated specimen set (2 coins) £14
1989 De luxe proof set 1p – £1 and Rights pair
(9 coins)   £35
1989 Standard proof set (9 coins)   £30
1989 Uncirculated specimen set 1p –
Scottish £1 (7 coins)   £18
1990 Britannia proof set (4 coins)   £800

1990 Proof set half sovereign – £5 (4 coins)
£825
1990 Proof set half sovereign – £2 (3 coins)
£360
1990 Proof set silver 5p both sizes (2 coins)
£20
1990 De luxe proof set 1p – £1, both 5p
(8 coins) £32
1990 Standard proof set (8 coins) £24
1990 Uncirculated specimen set (8 coins) £15
1991 Britannia proof set (4 coins) £760
1991 Proof set half sovereign – £5 (4 coins)
£1200
1991 Proof set half sovereign – £2 (3 coins)
£435
1991 De luxe proof set 1p – £1 (7 coins) £30
1991 Standard proof set (7 coins) £25
1991 Uncirculated specimen set (7 coins) £16
1992 Britannia proof set (4 coins) £775
1992 Proof set half sovereign – £5 (4 coins)
£950
1992 Proof set half sovereign – £2 (3 coins)
£450
1992 De luxe proof set 1p – £1, both 10p and
50p (9 coins) £35
1992 Standard proof set (9 coins) £30
1992 Uncirculated specimen set (9 coins) £15
1993 Britannia proof set (4 coins) £900
1993 Proof set half sovereign – £5 (4 coins)
£1200
1993 Proof set half sovereign – £2 (3 coins)
£500
1993 De luxe proof set 1p – £1 and Coronation
£5 (8 coins) £40
1993 Standard proof set (8 coins) £35
1993 Uncirculated specimen set 1p – £1 and
EC 50p (8 coins) £15
1993 Britannia proof set (4 coins) £825
1994 Proof set half sovereign – £5 (4 coins)
£1250
1994 Proof set half sovereign – £2 (3 coins)
£550
1994 De luxe proof set 1p – Bank of England
£2 (8 coins) £35
1994 Standard proof set (8 coins) £30
1994 Uncirculated set 1p – £1 and Normandy
50p (7 coins) £15
1995 Britannia proof set (4 coins) £800
1995 Proof set half sovereign – £5 (4 coins)
£1250
1995 Proof set half sovereign – £2 (3 coins)
£500
1995 De luxe proof set 1p – Peace £2 (8 coins)
£35

1995 Standard proof set (8 coins) £30
1995 Uncirculated specimen set (8 coins) £15
1996 Britannia proof set (4 coins) £950
1996 Proof set half sovereign – £5 (4 coins)
£1250
1996 Proof set half sovereign – £2 (3 coins)
£520
1996 De luxe set 1p – £2 and Queen's
Birthday
£5 (9 coins) £40
1996 Standard proof set (9 coins) £35
1996 Uncirculated specimen set 1p – £2
Football (8 coins) £15
1996 Silver proof set, decimal 25th
Anniversary (7 coins) £125
1997 Britannia silver proof set (4 coins) £100
1997 Proof set half sovereign – £5 (4 coins)
£1250
1997 Proof set half sovereign – £2 (3 coins)
£520
1997 De luxe set 1p – £2 and Golden Wedding
£5 (10 coins) £50
1997 Standard proof set (10 coins) £36
1997 Uncirculated specimen set (10 coins) £16
1997 Proof silver set 50p both sizes (2 coins)
£50
1998 Britannia gold proof set (4 coins) £1100
1998 Britannia silver proof set (4 coins) £100
1998 Proof set half sovereign – £5 (4 coins)
£1250
1998 Proof set half sovereign – £2 (3 coins)
£500
1998 De luxe set 1p – £2 and Prince of Wales
£5 (10 coins) £40
1998 Standard proof set (10 coins) £36
1998 Uncirculated specimen set (10 coins) £15
1999 Britannia gold set (4 coins) £1250
1999 Proof set half sovereign – £5 (4 coins)
£1275
1999 Proof set half sovereign – Rugby £3
(3 coins) £500
1999 De luxe proof set 1p – Diana £5 (9 coins)
£48
1999 Standard proof set (9 coins) £36
1999 Uncirculated specimen set 1p – £2
(8 coins) £15
2000 Britannia gold proof set (4 coins) £1250
2000 Proof set half sovereign – £5 (4 coins)
£1275
2000 Proof set half sovereign – £2 (3 coins)
£500
2000 Millennium de luxe proof set 1p – £5
(10 coins) £50
2000 Standard proof set (10 coins) £35

2000 Millennium Time Capsule (9 coins)	£25
2000 Uncirculated specimen set (9 coins)	£12
2000 Queen Mother silver piedfort crown	£70
2000 Public Libraries silver piedfort 50p	£50
2001 Britannia gold proof set (4 coins)	£830
2001 Proof set half sovereign – £5	£1250
2001 Proof set half sovereign – £2	£550
2001 Executive proof set, 1p – £5 (10 coins)	£70
2001 De luxe proof set (10 coins)	£48
2001 Gift proof set (10 coins)	£42
2001 Standard proof set (10 coins)	£35
2001 Uncirculated specimen set (10 coins)	£15
2001 Marconi piedfort £2	£30
2001 Northern Ireland silver proof £1	£20
2001 Northern Ireland silver piedfort £1	£35
2002 Britannia gold proof set (4 coins)	
2002 Proof set half sovereign – £5 (4 coins)	
2002 Proof set half sovereign – £2 (3 coins)	
2002 De luxe proof set	
2002 Standard proof set	
2002 Uncirculated specimen set	
2003 Britannia gold proof set (4 coins)	£800
2003 Proof set half sovereign – £5 (4 coins)	£895
2003 Proof set half sovereign – £2 (3 coins)	£425
2003 De luxe proof set	
2003 Standard proof set	
2003 Uncirculated specimen set	
2003 WSPU 50p silver proof	£35
2003 WSPU 50p silver piedfort	£45
2003 WSPU 50p gold proof	£240
2003 DNA £2 uncirculated specimen folder	£5
2003 DNA £2 silver proof	£25
2003 DNA £2 silver piedfort	£45
2003 DNA £2 gold proof	£275
2003 Coronation Anniversary £5 uncirculated specimen	£10

SCOTLAND

From the evidence of coin hoards and stray finds it is clear that although the Scots had no coins of their own a thousand years after coins began to circulate in southern Britain they were no strangers to coinage. Moreover, in the offshore islands and the far north of Scotland, under Norse rule till 1266, the numerous Viking hoards are a mute reminder of their raids on England, Ireland and farther afield, judging by the presence of Frankish deniers and Arab dirhems among this booty. Nevertheless, the lack of an indigenous coinage reflects a tribal society and its subsistence economy. Not until the 12th century did a Scottish coinage emerge under rulers who were descended from the Anglo-Saxon princess Margaret and who imported ideas from the south regarding law and government. Margaret's son David invited Norman mercenaries to subdue his unruly Celtic subjects and with them they brought the feudal system, laws and customs, and, above all, the notion of coined money.

Thereafter the coinage of Scotland followed the pattern of England, with silver pennies of a similar design, a stylised portrait on the obverse and a cross on the reverse. The Scottish mints were mainly in the south of the country and included Carlisle and Berwick, both Scottish towns at that period. Today, Roxburgh is a mere village but in the Middle Ages it was an important stronghold and one of the chief mints along with Edinburgh. Alexander III introduced the long cross penny following the recoinage of 1279 in England, and in this period no fewer than 18 mints were in operation. The first silver halfpennies and farthings appeared in the same reign while, at the other extreme, the first gold coin was the noble, introduced by David II who also struck the first larger silver coins, an impressive series of groats.

In the reign of James III (1460–88) the first coins to bear a realistic portrait appeared reflecting the Continental influence (mainly French) on Scotland at that time. The portrait groats and half groats of 1484 anticipated the testoons of Henry VII by some 16 years. In the same period, Scotland introduced subsidiary coins in copper or brass. The coinage became increasingly complex in the 16th century, with many different denominations. The troubled reign of Mary Queen of Scots is charted numismatically by the coins before marriage, in the names of Mary and Francis or Mary and Henry Lord Darnley, interspersed by the coins of her first and second widowhood. The coins of her son James VI present a bewildering array of denominations from the tiny copper hardhead to the magnificent £20 gold piece of 1575.

Scotland continued to have its own coins for more than a century after James ascended the English throne in 1603 but the union of the crowns had major repercussions on the Scottish coinage, from the reference to Great Britain and the inclusion of his English and French titles. Distinctive coins continued in the reigns of Charles I and included some milled coins struck by Nicholas Briot when he was sent to Edinburgh to re-organise the mint. The reign of Charles II is memorable for the closure of the Scottish mint (1682–87) for corrupt practices and criminal activities of its officials. Under James II the Mint was re-opened and struck milled silver coins. The unusual denominations of Scottish coins latterly is explained by the depreciation of the currency against sterling, so that the Scottish shilling was worth only an English penny. Conversely the English crown of five shillings was represented north of the border by the 60 shilling piece.

The Act of Union in 1707 integrated Scotland politically with England and led to the closure of the Scottish parliament. The Edinburgh mint survived a few years longer and struck coins of the standard English (now British) type, identifiable by the initial E below the bust of Queen Anne. Although the coins of 1709 were the last distinctive coins struck in Scotland, a number of patterns or restrikes are known from dies that were prepared at the time of the first Jacobite uprising, and though they were not actually struck until 1828 they are not without considerable interest to collectors.

As in England, tradesmen's tokens circulated widely in the late 18th and early 19th centuries during the chronic shortage of regal subsidiary coinage. Similarly, a wide range of Spanish dollars was countermarked, and in 1811–12 numerous silver tokens were struck from melted down Spanish coins. These countermarked and restruck pieces are outside the scope of this catalogue. Coins in this section are priced in Fine and Very Fine condition only.

David I (1124–53)

Penny, Berwick, various types from
£450 £1200
Penny, Carlisle, various types from
£500 £1300
Penny, Edinburgh, various types from
£600 £1500

Penny, Roxburgh, various types from
£750 £1500

Prince Henry, Earl of Northumberland and Huntingdon (1139–52)

Coins struck by David's son as an English magnate during the wars between Stephen and Matilda.
Penny, Corbridge   £1600   —
Penny, Carlisle   —   —
Penny, Bamborough, two types, from
£1200 £3250

Malcolm IV (1153–65)

Penny, Roxburgh, five types, from
£3500 £10000
Penny, Berwick, type III only
£4000   —

William the Lion (1165–1214)

Penny, crescent and pellet type, no mint name, from   £150 £250
Penny, with mint name Berwick, Edinburgh, Perth or Roxburgh, from   £100 £175
Penny, short cross and stars, head left, from
£250 £450

Penny, similar but head left, Roxburgh only
£400   £700

Alexander II (1214–49)

Penny, Berwick or Roxburgh, various types from
£700   £1500

Alexander III (1249–86)

1250–80. First coinage.

Obv: Left-facing profile ALEXANDER REX. Rev: Long cross with stars in the angles. Mint and moneyer's name.

Penny, Aberdeen	£100	£260
Penny, Ayr	£100	£325
Penny, Berwick, various from	£70	£160
Penny, Dun(fermline?)	£130	£360
Penny, Edinburgh, various from	£50	£160
Penny, Forfar	£125	£425
Penny, Forres	£140	£400
Penny, Glasgow	£150	£430
Penny, Inverness	£150	£400
Penny, Kinghorn	£175	£430
Penny, Lanark	£150	£380
Penny, Montrose	£250	£500
Penny, Perth, various from	£70	£170
Renfrew	£175	£525
Roxburgh, various from	£70	£180
St Andrews	£100	£235
Stirling	£140	£450

1280–86. Second Coinage.

Obv: Left-facing crowned head. Rev: Long cross with six-pointed mullets in angles. No mint name.

Farthing, two types from	£175	£450
Halfpenny, three types from	£80	£200
Penny, ESCOSSIE REX, several types from	£60	£100
Penny, REX SCOTORVM, nine types from	£35	£80

John Baliol (1292–96)

1292. First Coinage.

Rough surface. JOHANNES DE GRA. Rev: Cross with mullets, REX SCOTORVM.

Halfpenny, two types from	£450	—
Penny, four types from	£130	£300

1294. Second Coinage.

Smooth surface, neater lettering and detail.

Halfpenny, two types from	£200	£500
Penny, three types from	£160	£325

Robert Bruce (1306–29)

Obv: Left-facing crowned head. ROBERTVS DEI GRA. Rev: Cross with mullets in angles.

Farthing	£1200	—
Halfpenny	£335	£850

Penny	£260	£750

David II (1329–71)

1330–56. First Coinage.

Obv: Left-facing crowned head. MONETA REGIS. Rev: Cross with mullets in angles.

Farthing, three types from	£900	£1700
Halfpenny, six types, from	£250	£600
Penny, large lettering	£80	£175
Penny, small lettering	£50	£125

1357–67. Second Coinage.

Obv: Left-facing crowned bust with sceptre. Rev: Cross and mullets. Heavy coinage based on the groat of 72 grs.

Penny, Aberdeen small young bust	£400	£750
Penny, Aberdeen, large young bust	£750	£1200
Penny, Edinburgh, small young bust	£70	£120
Penny, Edinburgh, large young bust, various types from	£90	£200
Penny, Edinburgh, older head, three types from	£100	£250
Half groat, Aberdeen, small young bust	£450	£800
Half groat, Aberdeen, large young bust	£850	£2000
Half groat, Edinburgh, small young bust	£65	£110
Half groat, Edinburgh, large young bust, three types from	£60	£100
Half groat, Edinburgh, older head, three types from	£80	£180

Groat, Aberdeen, small young bust	£450	£800
Groat, Aberdeen, large young bust	£750	£1200
Groat, Edinburgh, small young bust, four types from	£75	£180
Groat, Edinburgh, large young bust, three types from	£140	£300
Groat, Edinburgh, older head, five types from	£90	£200
Noble, as English type but REX SCOTORVM	—	—

1367–71. Third Coinage.

Lighter than previous issue, based on the groat of 61 grs. Designs similar to the previous issue but a star behind the king's head or at the foot of the sceptre. Only struck at Edinburgh.

Penny, two types from	£85	£200
Half groat, three types from	£80	£200
Groat, three types from	£50	£120

Robert II (1371–90)

Obv: Left-facing crowned head with sceptre. Rev: Cross with mullets.

Halfpenny, Edinburgh	£125	£400
Halfpenny, Dundee	—	—
Penny, Edinburgh, four types from	£75	£180
Penny, Dundee	—	—
Penny, Perth	£200	£400
Half groat, Edinburgh, three types from	£120	£340
Half groat, Dundee	£350	£600
Half groat, Perth, two types from	£80	£200
Groat, Edinburgh, four types from	£100	£220
Groat, Dundee	£350	£600

Groat, Perth, two types from   £120   £250

Robert III (1390–1406)

1390–1403. Heavy Coinage.

Obv: Full-face bust. Rev: Cross with three pellets in angles (silver). Based on the groat of 46 grs and lion of 61 grs.
Obv: Crowned shield. Rev: St Andrew (gold).

Half groat, Edinburgh, three types from	£125	£350
Half groat, Perth	£230	£500
Groat, Edinburgh, four types from	£60	£180
Groat, Aberdeen, two types from	£240	£500
Groat, Perth, two types from	£185	£320
Demy-lion (2s 6d)	—	—
Lion (5s), two types from	£600	£1100

1403–06. Light Coinage.

As above, but based on the groat of 28 grs and the lion of 38 grs. Halfpenny and penny of debased silver.

Halfpenny, Edinburgh, two types from	£250	£450
Halfpenny, Perth	£350	£700
Penny, Edinburgh, four types from	£150	£300
Penny, Aberdeen	£375	£800
Penny, Perth	£280	£500
Groat, Edinburgh, two types from	£300	£650
Groat, Aberdeen	£750	£2000
Groat, Dumbarton	£600	£1500
Demy-lion, smaller and lighter types from	£750	£1200
Lion, two types from	£850	£2500

James I (1406–37)

Silver groats and billon coins: as previous issues.
Obv: Lion rampant in lozenge. Rev: Saltire cross in tressure (gold).

Halfpenny, Edinburgh, two types from	£125	£400
Penny, Edinburgh, seven types from	£120	£380
Penny, Aberdeen, two types from	£850	—
Penny, Inverness, two types	—	—
Groat, Edinburgh, small neat bust, three types from	£125	£270
Groat, Edinburgh, large crude bust	£150	£300
Groat, Linlithgow, small neat bust	£350	£600
Groat, Linlithgow, large crude bust	£400	£750
Groat, Perth, small neat bust	£250	£550
Groat, Perth, large crude bust	£350	£650
Half demy (4s 6d)	£450	£800
Demy (9s), four types from	£350	£750

James II (1437–60)

1437–51. First Coinage.

Penny (16 grs), Edinburgh	—	—
Penny (16 grs), Stirling	—	—
Groat (6d, 64 grs), Edinburgh, no ornaments, three types from	£450	£850
Groat, Edinburgh, mantled bust, ornate crown	£185	£500
Groat, Linlithgow	—	—
Groat, Stirling	—	—
Demy, three types from	£375	£750

1451–60. Second Coinage.

Penny (10 grs), Edinburgh, five types from	£175	£550
Penny, Aberdeen	—	—
Penny, Perth	—	—
Penny, Roxburgh	—	—
Half groat (6d), Edinburgh, mm cross / crown	£360	£800
Half groat, Aberdeen	—	—
Half groat, Perth	—	—
Groat (12d, 59 grs), Edinburgh, eight types from	£150	£500
Groat, Aberdeen	£700	—
Groat, Perth	—	—
Groat, Roxburgh	£1750	—
Half lion (5s), uncrowned shield	£450	£800
Half lion, small crown over shield	£650	£950

Lion (10s) crowned shield, three types from	£475	£1500

James III (1460–88)

1460–83. Light Coinage.

Farthing, regal copper, two types from	£160	£450
Farthing, Bishop Kennedy pauper money, three types from	£180	£425
Halfpenny, billon, Edinburgh	—	—
Penny, billon, Edinburgh, four types from	£100	£350
Penny, brass, Bishop Kennedy, five types from	£125	£375
Half plack (2d), .500 silver, Edinburgh, three types from	£95	£260
Penny (3d), .925 silver, Edinburgh, two types from	£100	£350
Plack (4d) .500 silver, Edinburgh, three types from	£80	£300
Half groat (6d), .925 silver, Edinburgh, three types from	£320	£850
Half groat (6d), Berwick, two types from	£750	£1200
Groat (12d), .925 silver, 40 grs, Edinburgh (c1467), three types	£300	£650
Groat (12d), as above, Berwick	£850	—
Groat (6d), .770 silver, 33 grs, Edinburgh (1471–83), two types	£160	£450
Groat (12d), .925 silver, 33 grs, Edinburgh, three types from	£200	£500
Groat (12d), as above, Berwick, two types from	£550	£900
Quarter rider (5s 9d)	£1700	£5000
Half rider (11s 6d), two types from	£1250	£3250
Rider (23s), three types from	£900	£2000

1484–88. Heavy Coinage.

Half groat (7d), .925 silver, Edinburgh
	£340	£800

Groat (1s 2d), .925 silver, Edinburgh, five types
from £160 £375
Groat, Aberdeen, two types from £225 £750
Unicorn (18s) £1800 £4000

James IV (1488–1513)

1489–96. Heavy Coinage.

Penny (billon), five types from	£50	£125
Half plack, four types from	£75	£200
Plack, four types from	£40	£120
Half groat, two types from	£300	£650
Groat, six types from	£300	£600
Half unicorn (9s), five types from	£800	£1750
Unicorn (18s), five types from	£675	£1500

1496–1513. Light Coinage.

Penny (3d)	£400	£100
Half groat (6d), three types from	£600	£120
Groat (12d), seven types from	£450	£80
Half lion (6s 8d), two types from	£1500	£350
Lion (13s 4d), two types from	£850	£175

James V (1513–42)

1513–26. First Coinage

Plack, two types from	£40	£13
Half unicorn (10s)	£1400	£300
Unicorn (20s), three types from	£700	£180

1526–39. Second Coinage.

Third groat (6d)	£140	£33
Groat (1s 6d), four types from	£100	£22
Crown (20s), five types from	£500	£125

1539–42. Third Coinage.

Quarter bawbee (1½d)	—	—
Half bawbee (3d), three types from	£75	£17
Bawbee (6d)	£30	£10

Third ducat (13s 4d)	£2000	£4000
Two-third ducat (26s 8d)	£1800	£3250
Ducat or Bonnet piece (40s), 1539-40, from		
	£1450	£4250

Mary (1542–67)

1542–58. First period: before marriage.

Lion (1½d), crowned M / lion, 1555–58, from		
	£35	£90
Penny (3d), crowned baby / cross (1547), two types from		
	£150	£450
Half bawbee (3d), crowned thistle / saltire cross, two types from		
	£75	£185
Plack (4d), crowned shield / ornate cross		
	£35	£90
Bawbee (6d), Edinburgh, crowned thistle MR / saltire, two types	£45	£100
Half testoon (2s), 1556-58, various types from		
	£160	£450
Testoon (4s), crowned bust / shield		
	£1000	£4000
Testoon, crowned M / shield, two types from		
	£300	£650
Testoon, crowned shield / cross potent,		

1566–58, various from	£250	3450
Twenty shillings, crowned shield / crowned MR, 1543	£2000	£5000
Crown (22s), crowned shield / cross fleury and thistles	£800	£2350
Half lion (22s), lion / Crowned MR, 1553		
	£450	£1459
Half ryal (30s), uncrowned bust / crowned shield, 1555-58 from	£2750	£6500
Lion (44s), crowned shield / crowned MR, 1553, 1557, from	£800	£1900
Ryal (60s), uncrowned bust / crowned shield, 1555–58, from	£1750	£4500

1558–60. Second period: Francis and Mary.

Hardhead (1½d), crowned FM, 1558-60, from		
	£35	£80
Nonsunt (12d), crowned FM / placard, 1558-59, from	£100	£260
Half testoon (2s 6d), dauphin's arms / crowned FM, 1558-9	£250	£750
Half testoon, crowned arms of France and Scotland, 1560–61	£200	£500
Testoon (5s) dauphin's arms / crowned FM, 1558–59 from	£175	£450
Testoon, crowned arms of France and Scotland, 1558–60, from	£160	£450
Ducat, Francis and Mary / Lorraine crosses, 1558	—	—

1560–65. Third period: first widowhood.

Half testoon, bonnet bust / arms of France and
Scotland, 1561–2   £850   £2250
Testoon, similar, 1561–62, from   £750   £2200

1565–67. Fourth period: Henry and Mary.

Testoon (5s), crowned shield / crowned mono-
gram, 1565   —   —
Third ryal (10s), crowned shield / tortoise and
palm tree, 1565–6   £300   £600
Two third ryal (20s), as above, 1565–67, from
                               £225   £650
Two third ryal, undated   £750   £1750
Ryal (30s) Henry and Mary / crowned shield,
1565   —   —
Ryal, crowned shield / tortoise and palm tree,
1565–67, from   £280   £750

1567. Fifth period: second widowhood.

Third ryal (10s), as above but REGINA MARIA
alone, 1566–7   £200   £52
Two third ryal (20s), as above, 1567
                               £250   £55
Ryal (30s), as above, 1567   £250   £60

James VI (1567–1603)

1567–71. First Coinage.

Third ryal (10s), crowned shield / crowned
sword, 1567–71 from   £180   £500

Two third ryal (20s), 1567–71, from
                 £175   £460

Ryal (30s), 1567–71, from   £200   £550

1571–80. Second Coinage.

Hardhead of Mary, countermarked (1575), from
                   £60   £100

Hardhead of Francis and Mary (1575), countermarked, from   £60   £120

Plack of Mary, countermarked (1575)
                £100   £300

Quarter merk (3s 4d), crowned shield / ornate
cross, 1572–80 from   £150   £280

Half merk (6s 8d), 1572–80, from £150   £300

Merk (13s 4d), crowned shield / thistle, 1579–80
                £750   £1200

Two merks (26s 8d), as above, 1578-80, from
                £850   £1700

Twenty pounds, half length bust / crowned
shield, 1575–76 from   £16000 £40000

1578. Revalued Coinage.
Coins countermarked with a crowned thistle.

Half testoon of 1556–57 (3s 8d)   £275   ——
Testoon of 1556–57 (7s 4d)   £220   ——

Testoon of Dauphin Francis and Mary, 1558–9 (7s 4d) £250 —

Testoon of King Francis and Mary, 1560 (7s 4d) £265 —

Third ryal of Henry and Mary (12s 3d) £500 —

Third ryal of Mary along (12s 3d) £425 —

Third sword ryal of 1567 (12s 3d) £450 —

Two third ryal of Henry and Mary (24s 6d) £325 —

Two third ryal of Mary alone (24s 6d) £350 —

Two third sword ryal (24s 6d) £400 —

Ryal of Henry and Mary (36s 9d) £375 —

Ryal of Mary alone (36s 9d) £525 —

Ryal or Sword dollar (36s 9d) £350 —

1580–81. Third Coinage.

Two shillings, crowned shield / crowned thistle, 1581 — —

Four shillings, 1581 £1150 £2400

Eight shillings, 1581 £900 £2200

Sixteen shillings, 1581 £1450 £3500

Ducat (80s), Ruffed bust / crowned shield, 1580 £2750 £6000

1582–88. Fourth Coinage.

Half plack (4d), crowned shield / thistle, (1583–90) three types from £100 £22●

Plack (8d) as above (1583–90), three types from £50 £12●

Ten shillings, half length in armour / crowned shield, 1582–4 from £120 £30●

Twenty shillings, 1582–85 from £140 £42●

Thirty shillings, 1581–86 from £175 £70●

Forty shillings, 1582 £2350 £750●

Third lion noble (25s), crowned lion/ crowned lrs, 1584 £3250 £650●

Two third lion noble (50s), 1584–85, 1587 from £3000 £650●

Lion noble (75s), 1584–86, 1568 from £2100 £590●

1588. Fifth Coinage.

Half hardhead (1d), crowned IR / lion rampant
£250   £500
Hardhead (2d), crowned IR / crowned shield
£300   £550
Hardhead (2d), crowned IR / lion rampant
£55   £180
Thistle noble (146s 6d), crowned shield on ship / thistle & sceptres   £1250   £3000

1591–93. Sixth Coinage.

Quarter merk (3s 4d), crowned shield / balance and sword, 1591   £250   £575
Half merk (6s 8d), 1591–93 from £160   £400
Hat piece (80s), bust in tall hat / crowned seated lion, 1591–93   £2500   £6000

1593–1601. Seventh Coinage.

Penny (1d), bareheaded bust / three thistles
(1597)   £275   £600
Turner (2d)   £125   £400
Saltire plack (4d), thistle over two sceptres / thistle lozenge   £150   £360
Twelve pence, bareheaded bust / triple-headed thistle, 1594–6 from   £60   £240
Thirty pence, 1594–1601 from   £75   £240
Five shillings, 1593–1601 from   £110   £300
Ten shillings, 1593–1601 from   £100   £275
Half rider (50s), king on horseback / crowned shield, 1593–1601 from   £350   £750
Rider (100s), 1593–1601 from   £420   £950

1601–4. Eighth Coinage.

Eighth thistle merk (1s 8d), crowned shield / thistle, 1601–3 from   £45   £160
Quarter thistle merk (3s 4d), 1601–4 from
£40   £145
Half thistle merk (6s 8d), 1601–4 from
£40   £150
Thistle merk (13s 4d), 1601–4 from
£50   £190
Half sword and sceptre piece (60s), 1601–4 from   £225   £375
Sword and sceptre piece (120s), 1601–4 from
£300   £500

After Accession to the English Throne (1603).

First shield (1604–9): English arms in first and fourth quarters.
Second shield (1609–25): Scottish arms in first and fourth quarters.

Penny, two types from	£35	£70
Twopence, two types from	£35	£75
Shilling (1d stg.), rose / thistle	£75	£280
Two shillings (2d stg.), crowned rose / crowned thistle	£50	£245
Six shillings (6d stg.), crowned bust / first shield, 1605–9 from	£350	£700
Six shillings, as above but second shield, 1610–22 from	£150	£500
Twelve shillings (1s stg.), first shield	£200	£600
Twelve shillings (1s stg.), second shield	£100	£250
Thirty shillings (2s 6d stg.), horseman / first shield	£120	£300
Thirty shillings (2s 6d stg,), second shield	£85	£200
Half crown (2s 6d stg.) gold, crowned bust first shield	£275	£500
Thistle crown (4s stg.), crowned rose / crowned thistle	£275	£500
Sixty shillings (5s stg.), horseman / first shield	£275	£600
Sixty shillings (5s stg.), second shield	£285	£650
Britain crown (5s stg.), crowned bust, first shield	—	—
Britain crown (5s stg.), second shield	£425	£850
Double crown (10s stg.), crowned bust / first shield	—	—
Double crown (10s stg.), second shield	£450	£1200
Unit (£1 stg.), half length armoured bust / first shield	£700	£2000
Unit (£1 stg.) second shield	£550	£900

Charles I (1625–49)

1625–36. First Coinage.

Penny, triple-headed thistle / lion rampant (1629)	£70	£120
Turner, as above (1629)	£15	£3
Shilling (1d stg.) crowned rose / crowned thistle	—	—
Two shillings (2d stg.), as above	£70	£320

Six shillings (6d stg.), crowned bust / shield,
1625–8, 1630–4 from   £110   £380
Twelve shillings (1s stg.) as above but undated
                                      £60   £180
Thirty shillings (2s 6d stg.)   £65   £245
Sixty shillings (5s stg.)   £360   £700
Britain crown (5s stg.)   —   —
Double crown (10s stg.)   £1300   £2800
Unit (20s stg.)   £550   £1250

1632–39. Susbsidiary Coinage.

Copper coins produced by the Earl of Stirling
under royal licence.
Turner (2d), Scottish crown over monogram /
thistle, four types   £20   £70
Turner, Scottish crown, many types from
                                      £12   £65

1636. Second Coinage.

Obv: Left-facing crowned bust. Rev: Crowned
shield.
Coins struck at Edinburgh under the supervi-
sion of Nicholas Briot. In addition to the ham-
mered coins a small quantity of milled patterns
were also produced.
Twenty pence (hammered)   £50   £325
Twenty pence (milled)   —   —
Forty pence (hammered)   £45   £160
Forty pence (milled)   —   —
Half merk (6s 8d stg.)   £60   £200
Half merk (milled)   —   —

1637–42. Third Coinage.

Coins with initials B or F denote Nicholas Briot
and his son-in-law, John Falkiner, who suc-
ceeded him as mint master in 1646.
Penny   —   —
Twopence, thistle over CR / thistle, three types
from   £25   £80
Threepence, interlinked Cs / thistle, two types
                                    —   —
Two shillings (2d stg.), bust / crowned shield,
three types from   £45   £150
Three shillings (3d stg.), as above £40   £135
Twenty pence, bust left / crowned thistle,
12 types from   £25   £70
Forty pence, as above, six types from
                                    £30   £90
Six shillings (6d stg.), bust left / crowned shield,
eight types from   £60   £180
Half merk (6s 8d Scots), bust left / crowned
shield, two types from   £50   £160

Twelve shillings (1s stg.), as above, seven types
from £65 £200
Thirty shillings (2s 6d stg.), horseman / crowned
shield, six types from £65 £200
Sixty shillings (5s stg.), as above £300 £850
Britain half crown (2s 6d stg.), bust / crowned
shield, two types £350 £1100
Britain crown (5s stg.), as above, two types
£850 £2250
Half unit (10s stg.), as above, two types from
£675 £1800
Unit (20s stg.), as above, three types from
£575 £1500

Charles II (1649–85)

Charles II was proclaimed King of Scots a few
weeks after his father's execution and was
crowned at Scone in January 1651, but the
defeat of the Royalists at Worcester (September
1651) drove the king into exile. Cromwell closed
the Edinburgh mint and thereafter no coins
were struck in Scotland till after the
Restoration.

1664–75. First Coinage.

Obv: Right-facing laureated bust. Rev:
Cruciform shields with interlinked Cs in angles.
Half merk, thistle below bust, 1664–73, from
£60 £200
Half merk, F below bust, 1674–75, from
£45 £160
Merk (13s 4d Scots), thistle below bust,
1664–6, 1668-74, from £45 £150
Merk, F below bust, 1674–75, from
£60 £200
Merk, no mark below bust, 1675
£55 £180
Two merks (26s 8d Scots), thistle above head,
1664 £185 £525
Two merks, thistle below bust, 1664, 1670,
1673–74, from £155 £450
Two merks, F below bust, 1673–75, from
£160 £450
Four merks (53s 4d Scots), thistle above bust,
1664 £300 £700

Four merks, thistle below bust, 1664–65, 1670, 1673, from £185 £550

Four merks, F below bust, 1674–75
£190 £500

1675–82. Second Coinage.

Obv: Left-facing laureated bust. Rev: St Andrew's cross (1/16 dollar) or cruciform crowned shields with thistles in the angles (other silver coins). Different motifs on the copper coins noted below.

Turner (2d Scots), crown over crossed swords / thistle, 1677–79 £30 £120

Turner, crowned monogram / thistle (1683)
£30 £120

Bawbee (6d Scots), bust / crowned thistle, 1677–79, from £45 £150

Sixteenth dollar (3s 4d Scots), 1677–81, from
£40 £120

Eighth dollar (6s 8d Scots), 1676–80, 1682, from £55 £160

Quarter dollar (13s 4d Scots), 1675–77, 1679–82, from £75 £220

Half dollar (26s 8d Scots), 1675–76, 1681, from
£170 £450

Dollar (53s 4d Scots),1676, 1679–82, from
£150 £350

James VII (1685–89)

The Edinburgh mint was not re-opened until 1687 and only struck silver coins in the last months of this reign.

Obv: Right-facing laureated bust. Rev: Cruciform shields (10s), crowned arms (others).

Ten shillings (10d stg.), 1687–88, from
£100 £275

Forty shillings (3s 4d stg.), 1687–88, from
£120 £325

Sixty shillings (5s stg.), 1688 — £1400

William and Mary (1689–94)

Obv: Conjoined left-facing busts. Rev: crowned thistle (copper), crowned entwined monograms (5s) or crowned shield (others).

Bodle (2d Scots), 1691–94   £40   £90
Bawbee (6d Scots), 1691–4, various mint-marks
from   £45   £135
Five shillings (5d stg.), 1691, 1694, from
    £70   £250
Ten shillings (10d stg.), 1689–92, 1694, from
    £50   £150
Twenty shillings (1s 8d stg.), 1693–94, from
    £120   £400
Forty shillings (3s 4d stg.), 1689–94, from
    £80   £250
Sixty shillings (5s stg.), 1691–92, from
    £150   £500

William III (1694–1702)

Obv: Crown over crossed sword and sceptre (bodle) or left-facing laureated bust (others) Rev: Crowned shield (gold and silver), or crowned thistle (copper). The pistole and half pistole were minted from gold imported by the Darien Company.

Bodle (2d Scots), flat sword and sceptre, 1695 four types from   £40   £150
Bodle, tall sword and sceptre, 1695–97, from
    £35   £120
Bawbee (6d Scots), 1697   £35   £130
Five shillings (5d stg.), 1695 GVL D G 1695–1701, from   £45   £150
Five shillings, GVLIELMVS DEI GRATIA, 1702
    £80   £325
Ten shillings (10d stg.), 1695–99, from
    £80   £240
Twenty shillings (1s 8d stg.), 1695–99, from
    £50   £220
Forty shillings (3s 4d stg.), 1695–1700, from
    £60   £250
Half pistole (£6 Scots), 1701   £1600   £4000
Pistole (£12 Scots), 1701   £1750   £4250

Queen Anne (1702–14)

The Act of Union (1707) brought Scottish independence to an end. The Edinburgh mint continued in operation till 1709, and after the Union struck coins of the English pattern, distinguished by the initial E below the queen's bust.

Before Union.

Obv: Left-facing bust.
Five shillings (5d stg.), crowned thistle 1705–06, from   £30   £120
Ten shillings (10d stg.), crowned shield 1705–06, from   £80   £260

After Union

	F	VF	EF
Sixpence, E below bust, 1707–8, from	£20	£50	£160
Sixpence, Edinburgh, E* below bust, 1708	£25	£65	£185
Sixpence, 'Edinburgh' bust, E*, 1708	£30	£70	£200
Shilling, 2nd bust E* below bust, 1707–8, from	£60	£140	£400
Shilling, 2nd bust, E below bust, 1707–8	£25	£50	£210
Shilling, 3rd bust, E below bust, 1707	£25	£60	£220
Shilling, 'Edinburgh' bust, E* below, 1707–9, from	£30	£100	£300
Half crown, E below bust, 1707–9, from	£65	£120	£375
Crown, 2nd bust, E below, 1707–8, from	£80	£240	£700

IRELAND

The earliest indigenous coins in Ireland were struck by the Vikings from about 995 till 1155. The Norman conquest of Ireland took place in the 1170s and thereafter English silver pennies were in circulation. However, these were augmented from time to time by distinctive coins, minted at Dublin, beginning with the silver pennies of 1185–99 under the authority of John, Lord of Ireland before he became King of England. Subsequent issues, in the names of English rulers as Lords of Ireland, follow the English patterns. Silver pennies predominated, with relatively few halfpence from the 14th century and groats from the reign of Edward IV. Shillings first appeared in 1552, while copper farthings were minted by Lord Harrington and the Duke of Lennox from 1613. There was a resurgence of distinctive coinage during the Civil War (1642–49) and a wide range of emergency pieces, such as Gun Money, during the Williamite War (1689–91). Something approaching a regular subsidiary coinage was produced from 1692 to 1823, with the effigy of the monarch on the obverse and a crowned harp reverse. Following the example of the Bank of England, the Bank of Ireland produced silver tokens in 1805–13 during a shortage of regal coinage.

Distinctive coins re-emerged in 1928. Most of these were struck to the same weights and specifications as the UK coinage and circulated freely in Northern Ireland until the Irish pound broke with sterling in the 1970s. As a member of the European single currency area, Ireland replaced its pound-pence system by the Euro in 2002.

We list only the commonest types of these and later coins and the reader is referred to Coincraft's *Standard Catalogue of Scotland, Ireland, Channel Islands & Isle of Man* for a more detailed and comprehensive coverage.

Hiberno-Norse Coinage (995–1150)

	F	VF
Penny, bust / cross, many types from	£100	£180

John, Lord of Ireland (1185–99)

Coins inscribed DOM(inus)

Farthing, various types from	£250	£600
Halfpenny, profile	£1400	—
Halfpenny, facing bust	£50	£100

John de Courcy, Lord of Ulster (1177–1205)

Farthing	£500	£1150
Halfpenny	—	—

John I (1199–1216)

Obv: Facing bust in a triangle inscribed JOHANNES REX. Rev: Sun, moon and stars in a triangle inscribed with the mint and moneyer's name. Dublin, Limerick and Waterford.

Halfpenny, from	£65	£150
Penny, from	£45	£90

Henry III (1216–72)

Penny, bust in triangle / long cross, Dublin, many types from	£40	£75

Edward I (1272–1307)

As previous type. Dublin, Cork and Waterford.

Farthing, several types from	£90	£235
Halfpenny, several types from	£40	£95
Penny, several types from	£40	£80

Edward III (1327–77)

Halfpenny, Dublin	—	—

Henry VI (1422–61)

Penny, Dublin	—	—

Edward IV (1461–83)

By far the most extensive and complex series of Irish coins. Farthings were minted in low-grade billon (almost entirely copper with very little silver). The range of coinage was extended in this period to include the groat and half groat. No fewer than seven distinct issues appeared in a 20 year period. The first coins bore no name, reflecting uncertainty as to who was actually on the throne when the Wars of the Roses were at their height.

1460–63. Anonymous Coinage.

Half farthing, small crown / cross	£800	—
Farthing, small crown / cross	£900	—
Farthing, large crown / cross	£1200	—
Penny, crown / cross and pellets, Dublin or Waterford	£750	—
Groat, crown / cross and pellets, Dublin, several types from	£275	£650

1463–65. Second Coinage.
As previous types but inscribed EDWARD(US) on obverse.

Half farthing, Patricius / Salvator	—	—
Farthing, Patricius / Salvator	£200	£1000
Penny, Dublin or Waterford	£1300	—
Half groat, Dublin	£950	—

1465–67. Third Coinage.
Obv: Small cross in centre of a rose. Rev: Radiant sun.

Groat, Dublin	£1000	—

1467–70. Fourth Coinage.
Obv: Crowned facing bust in fleured tressure. Rev: Rose on sunburst.

Farthing, shield / rose on sunburst
	£100 £500
Penny, Dublin or Drogheda	£1200 —
Half groat, Dublin	£1300 —
Groat, Dublin, Drogheda or Trim, from	
	£1450 —
Double groat, Dublin, Drogheda or Trim, from	
	£1600 £4000

1470–73. Fifth Coinage.
Obv: Crowned bust in tressure. Rev: Long cross with three pellets in each angle.

Halfpenny, Dublin	£600 —
Penny, Dublin, Galway, Limerick or Waterford, from	£70 £150
Half groat, Dublin, Galway or Trim, from	£400 £750
Groat, Dublin, five types from	£140 £500
Groat, Drogheda, four types from	£200 £650
Groat, Limerick or Trim, from	£300 —
Groat, Waterford, three types from	£250 £800

1473–78. Sixth Coinage.
As previous issue but coins about 25 per cent smaller and lighter.

Penny, Dublin, nine types from	£40 £100
Penny, Cork, two types	— —
Penny, Drogheda, eight types from	£45 £110
Penny, Limerick, two types from	£80 £200
Penny, Trim, four types from	£40 £100
Penny, Waterford, five types from	£40 £100
Half groat, Dublin, two types	— —
Half groat, Limerick, two types	— —
Half groat, Drogheda, Waterford or Wexford	— —
Groat, Dublin, six types from	£100 £350
Groat, Cork, two types	— —
Groat, Drogheda, four types from	£120 £360
Groat, Limerick, two typed from	£225 £600
Groat, Trim, three types from	£225 £650
Groat, Waterford, four types from	£135 £350
Groat, Wexford	— —

1478–83. Seventh Coinage.
Obv: Crowned bust flanked by sun and rose. Rev: Long cross with a rose in the centre and roses and suns in angles.

Penny, Dublin, three types from	£200 £1000
Groat, Dublin or Drogheda, from	£400 £850

Richard III (1483–85)

1483. First Coinage.
Types as above, but inscribed RICARDUS.

Penny	— —
Half groat	— —
Groat, Drogheda	£800 £2200

1483–85. Second Coinage.
Penny, bust / long cross, Dublin or Waterford, from	£500 £1500
Groat, shield / three crowns over a cross, Dublin or Waterford, from	£450 £120

Lambert Simnel, Pretender to the Throne as Edward V (1487)

Groat, as above but no king's name, Dublin or Waterford, from	£850 £2000

Henry VII (1485–1509)

1485–87. First Coinage.

Obv: Arms in shield, no king's name. Rev: Three crowns on a cross.

Halfpenny, Dublin	— —
Penny, Dublin	£400 £800
Half groat, Dublin, two types from	£180 £400
Groat, Dublin, three types from	£140 £350
Groat, Waterford, five types from	£140 £350

1487–90. Second Coinage.
As previous issue but very crude. Inscriptions: HENRICUS REX AN (obv.) DOMINUS VBERNIE (rev.)

Penny, Dublin, three types from	£375 £750
Half groat, Dublin, seven types from	£125 £330
Groat, Dublin, four types from	£65 £200

1496–1505. Third Coinage.
Obv: Crowned bust. Rev: Long cross with pellets in the angles. Crude versions of contemporary English coins with CIVITAS DUBLINE on the reverse.

Penny, four types from	£700	—
Half groat, three types from	£800	—
Groat, 13 types from	£90	£200

Henry VIII (1509–47)

1534–47. Harp Coinage.

Coins were struck mainly in London for use in Ireland. Obv: crowned shield. Rev: crowned harp flanked by HA, HI or HK alluding to Henry's wives Anne Boleyn, Jane Seymour and Katherine Howard respectively and latterly HR (Henricus Rex).

Half groat, three types (HA, HI or HK) from	£300	£700
Groat, many types (HA, HI, HK or HR) from	£60	£150
Groat, Bristol, two types from	£150	£300

1547–50. Posthumous Coinage.

Obv: Facing bust of Henry VIII. Rev: Armorial shield on a cross. Struck at Dublin.

Threefarthings	£475	£1250
Threehalfpence	£350	£900
Threepence, three types from	£90	£200
Sixpence, four types from	£75	£180

Edward VI (1547–53)

The first Irish coin to bear a date was this shilling bearing the date MDLII (1552) on the obverse. Obv: Right-facing crowned bust with harp mint-mark. Rev: Arms in oval shield.

Shilling (billon)	£700	£1500

Shilling (brass or copper), 'Bungal penny'	£120	—

Mary (1553–54)

Obv: Left-facing crowned bust. Rev: Crowned shield flanked MR.

Penny	—	—
Half groat	—	—
Groat	—	—
Shilling, MDLIII or MDLIIII, from	£475	£1250

Philip and Mary (1554–58)

Obv: Philip and Mary face to face. Rev: Crowned harp flanked by crowned P and M.

Groat, 1555–58, from	£80	£200
Shilling, 1555	£250	£850

Elizabeth I (1558–1603)

1558. Base Coinage.

Coins of .250 fine silver. Obv: Left-facing crowned bust. Rev: Crowned harp flanked by crowned monogram ER.

Groat	£125	£350
Shilling	£300	£850

1561. Fine Coinage.

Designs as above but struck in .916 fine silver.

Groat	£225	£550
Shilling	£150	£475

1601–3. Third Coinage.

Struck in copper or. 250 fine silver. Obv: Shield bearing arms of England and France in alternate quarters. Rev: Crowned harp.

Halfpenny, copper, 1601	£50	£150
Penny, copper, 1601-2 or undated, from		
	£30	£85
Threepence, copper	£120	£350
Sixpence, silver	£90	£200
Shilling, silver	£100	£400

James I (1603–25)

1603–4. First Coinage.

Obv: Right-facing bust with square beard. ANG SCO in legend. Rev: Crowned harp.

Sixpence	£70	£250
Shilling	£80	£300

1604–7. Second Coinage.

Obv: Right-facing bust with pointed beard. MAG BRIT in legend. Rev: Crowned harp.

Sixpence	£80	£280
Shilling	£95	£350

1613–25. Subsidiary Coinage.

Copper farthings struck by Lord Harrington and later by the Duke of Lennox under royal licence.

Farthing, Harrington, small size, two types from		
	£25	£80
Farthing, Harrington, large size	£15	£50
Farthing, Lennox, five types from	£15	£45

Charles I (1625–49)

No Irish coins were struck in the reign of Charles I until the outbreak of the Great Rebellion which erupted in 1641 and indirectly triggered off the Civil War in Britain (initially a showdown between King and Parliament over the costs of suppressing the uprising). The war in Ireland was not only between Royalists and Parliamentary forces but between Catholics and Protestants, and between native Irish and Anglo-Scottish settlers. The coins comprised the emergency issues in the name of King Charles authorised by Lord Inchiquin (1642) and the Marquess of Ormonde (1643–44) as lieutenants of Ireland, the coins issued by the Confederated Catholics (1642–44) and a number of base metal pieces produced as small change in the Protestant 'cities of refuge'. Ormonde also struck silver coins in 1649 in the name of Charles II after the execution of his father.

The only distinctive coins of Ireland in this reign prior to the Great Rebellion were copper farthings produced by the Duchess of Richmond and later Lord Matravers under royal licence. They were struck in London but intended specifically for circulation in Ireland and have the usual crowned harp reverse.

1625–34. Copper Coinage.

Farthing, Richmond, seven circular types from		
	£15	£50
Farthing, Richmond, two oval types from		
	£15	£50
Farthing, Maltravers, four circular types from		
	£20	£65
Farthing, Maltravers, oval type	£30	£70
Farthing, Rose type (smaller, thicker flan), seven types from		
	£16	£55

1642. Inchiquin Coinage.

Struck at Dublin from commandeered silver plate. Marked on both sides with the actual weight of the piece.

Groat	—	—
Sixpence	—	—
Ninepence	—	—
Shilling	—	—
Half crown	£1100	£2250
Crown	£1200	£2500

1643. Dublin Money.

Struck at Dublin. Rough pieces of plate crudely stamped with value on both sides.

Half crown	£350	£950
Crown	£550	£1600

1643–44. Ormonde Coinage.

Struck at Dublin from commandeered plate. Usually more regular in circular shape. Obv: Crown over CR. Rev: Value in Roman numerals.

Twopence	£320	£675
Threepence	£70	£160

Groat	£80	£200
Sixpence	£100	£235
Shilling	£100	£250
Half crown	£250	£650
Crown	£350	£750
Pistole	—	—
Double Pistole	—	—

1649. Dublin Money.

Struck by authority of the Marquess of Ormonde in the name of Charles II.
Obv: Large crown with CAR II D.G. MAG BRIT round circle. Rev: Value in Roman numerals, with FRA ET HYB REX F.D. round circle.

Half crown	£1300	£2800
Crown	£1800	£4750

Catholic Confederacy

1642–3. Kilkenny.

Obv: Crown and two sceptres with CARO D.G. MAG BRI round circle. Rev: Crowned harp with FRA ET HIB REX round circle.

Farthing	£200	£650
Halfpenny	£180	£500

1642. Blacksmith's Money.

Obv: King on horseback. Rev: Arms in an oval shield.
These very crude coins were struck in imitation of the Tower of London coinage.

Half crown, two types from	£400	£1000

1643–44. Rebel Money.

Obv: Crutched cross. Rev: Value in Roman numerals.

Half crown	£1450	£3250
Crown	£1200	£2750

Cities of Refuge.

Four towns in the province of Munster, besieged by the Catholic Confederacy.

Bandon (1646–47)

Obv: BB in circle of pellets. Rev: Three castles in circle of pellets.

Farthing	£450	—

Cork (1647)

Obv: CORK(E) in circle of pellets. Rev: Castle (copper). Obv: CORK / 1647. Rev: Value in Roman numerals (silver).

Farthing	£400	—
Halfpenny	£800	—
Sixpence	£550	£115
Shilling	£1100	£260

Kinsale (1647)

Obv: KS in circle of pellets. Rev: Chequered shield.

Farthing	£400	—

Youghal (1646)

Obv: YT with or without a date below. Rev: Galley in a double circle. Square format.

Farthing (copper), six square types from	£350	£95
Farthing (copper), circular type	£400	£100
Twopence (brass)	—	—
Threepence (pewter)	—	—

Charles II (1660–85)

1660–1. Sir Thomas Armstrong.

Obv: Crown on crossed sceptres. Rev: Crowned harp.

Farthing	£160	—

1668? St Patrick's Coinage.

Obv: Crown over King David playing the harp. Rev: St Patrick driving the snakes out of Ireland.

Farthing, six types from	£80	£150
Halfpenny, six types from	£150	£400

1679. Dublin Coinage.

Obv: Crowned harp. Rev: Shield containing three towers.

Halfpenny, 1679	—	—

1680. Regal Coinage.

Obv: Right-facing laureated bust. Rev: Crowned harp.

Halfpenny, large lettering, 1680–81, from	£60	£150
Halfpenny, small lettering, 1681–84, from	£25	£200

James II (1685–88)

1685–88. Regal Coinage.
Obv: Left-facing laureated bust. Rev: Crowned harp.
Halfpenny, 1685-88, from   £35   £125

1689–90. Emergency Coinage.
James II, who had gone into exile in France in 1688, led a French invasion of Ireland where he landed in March 1689. Needing money to pay his troops, James ordered the Dublin Mint to strike coins from copper or brass. Old cannon were melted down for this purpose, hence the name Gun Money by which the first issue is known. Unusually, these coins bear the month as well as year of minting. In March 1690 James decreed that 'white metal' (pewter) be coined, although coins in that alloy were issued with the date 1689 as well as 1690.

Gun Money.

Obv: King on horseback. Rev: Cruciform crowned shields (crown).
Obv: Left-facing laureated bust. Rev: Crown over crossed sceptres (others).
Sixpence, June 1689 – June 1690, from
     £35   £110
Shilling (25–27mm), July 1689 – April 1690, from   £12   £50
Shilling (22–24mm), April-September 1690, from   £12   £50
Half crown (31–32mm), July 1689 – May 1690, from   £25   £80
Half crown (27mm), April – October 1690, from
     £25   £75
Crown, 1690, 14 types from   £35   £100

Pewter Money.

Obv: King on horseback. Rev: Cruciform crowned shields (crown).
Obv: Left-facing laureated bust. Rev: Crowned harp (others).
Halfpenny, large bust, 1689–90, six types from
     £120   £350
Halfpenny, small bust, 1690   £140   £375
Penny, large bust, 1689–90, from £350   £850
Penny, small bust, 1690   £225   £550
Groat, 1689   £450   £1100
Crown, 1690, two types from   £600   £1400

Limerick Money.

Issued by the Jacobites in Limerick after James left Ireland.
Obv: Left-facing laureated bust. Rev: Seated figure of Hibernia.
Farthing, 1691, two types from   £45   £100
Halfpenny, 1691   £40   £95

William and Mary (1688–94)

	F	VF	EF

Obv: Right-facing conjoined busts. Rev: Crowned harp.
Halfpenny, 1692–94, six types from
| | £20 | £75 | £300 |

William III (1694–1702)

Obv: Right-facing laureated bust. Rev: Crowned harp.
Halfpenny, draped bust, 1696
| | £50 | £100 | — |
Halfpenny, undraped bust, 1696
| | £200 | £600 | — |

George I (1714–27)

Coins struck in London and later Bristol and issued by William Wood.
Obv: Right-facing laureated bust. Rev: Hibernia.
Farthing, Hibernia playing harp, 1722
| | £175 | £425 | £1000 |
Farthing, Hibernia holding palm, 1723–24, from
| | £50 | £140 | £275 |
Halfpenny, Hibernia playing harp, 1722
| | £40 | £100 | £250 |
Halfpenny, Hibernia holding palm, 1722–4, from
| | £15 | £60 | £160 |

George II (1727–60)

Obv: Left-facing laureated bust. Rev: Crowned harp.
Farthing, GEORGIUS, small lettering, 1737–38, from
| | £20 | £45 | £100 |

Farthing, GEORGIUS, large lettering, 1744
| | £20 | £45 | £120 |
Farthing, GEORGIVS, 1760
| | £15 | £30 | £80 |
Halfpenny, GEORGIUS, small lettering, 1736–38, from
| | £15 | £40 | £120 |
Halfpenny, GEORGIUS, large lettering, 1741-46, from
| | £20 | £45 | £125 |
Halfpenny, GEORGIVS, 1747-55, from
| | £20 | £45 | £125 |
Halfpenny, GEORGIVS, broad truncation, 1760
| | £15 | £40 | £120 |

George III (1760–1820)

Regal Coinage.

Obv: Right-facing laureated bust. Rev: Crowned harp. Copper.
Farthing, 1806
| | £10 | £20 | £50 |
Halfpenny, 1st bust, 1766, 1769
| | £15 | £40 | £100 |
Halfpenny, 2nd bust, 1769
| | £15 | £60 | £140 |
Halfpenny, 3rd bust, 1775–6, 1781–2, from
| | £18 | £40 | £115 |
Halfpenny, 4th bust, 1805
| | £5 | £10 | £35 |
Penny, 1805
| | £10 | £25 | £100 |

Bank of Ireland Tokens.

Obv: Right-facing laureated bust. BANK TOKEN and value in words Five and ten pence (or Hibernia holding a palm (thirty pence and six shillings). Silver.
Five pence, 1805–6, from
| | £12 | £25 | £70 |
Ten pence, 1st bust, 1805–6, from
| | £10 | £25 | £120 |

| Ten pence, 2nd bust, 1813 | £8 | £20 | £60 |

Thirty pence, 1808	£25	£70	£160
Six shillings, 1804, five types from			
	£100	£175	£450

GUERNSEY

The bailiwick of Guernsey in the Channel Islands used English and French coinage for centuries but the use of the latter died out during the Napoleonic Wars. The chronic shortage of coins during this period led to a number of tokens issued by tradesmen as well as a silver crown of the Bank of Guernsey. Subsidiary coinage in copper and denominated in doubles (8 = 1 penny) was introduced in 1830. Similar coins struck in bronze followed in the 1860s. A cupro-nickel threepence with a scalloped edge was introduced in 1956 and a ten-shilling piece portraying William the Conqueror was struck in 1966 to celebrate the ninth centenary of the Norman Conquest. Guernsey followed the United Kingdom in adopting decimal currency from 1969 onwards using the same weights and specifications. Bi-metallic £2 coins for general circulation were introduced in 1997 but previously crowns (formerly tariffed at 25 pence) were issued as £2 coins from 1985 to 1995 and as £5 from 1995 onward. A gold proof series (£10 to £100) was introduced in 1994. The island of Alderney, which forms part of the bailiwick of Guernsey, has issued a number of commemorative coins since 1993.

1809. Bank of Guernsey Token.

Silver, 42mm, overstruck on Spanish 8 reales. Obv: Shield in circle inscribed BISHOP DE JERSEY & CO. Rev: Wreath enclosing value in words with BANK OF GUERNSEY round the top.

| Five shillings, 1809 | — | — | — |

1830–1956. Double Coinage.

Obv: Heraldic shield. Rev: Value and date.

	VF	EF	Unc
Double, copper, 1830	£3	£12	£25
Double, bronze, 1868	£8	£22	£60
Double, Heaton, 1885–1911, various dates from			
	£1	£3	£12
Double, Heaton, new shield (leopards), 1911–38	£1	£3	£12
Two doubles, copper, 1858	£5	£30	£110
Two doubles, bronze, 1868, 1874, from			
	£7	£35	£120
Two doubles, Heaton, narrow shield, 1885–1911, from	£3	£10	£25
Two doubles, Heaton, broad shield, 1914–29, from	£2	£5	£18
Four doubles, copper, 1830, 1858, from			
	£4	£10	£35
Four doubles, bronze, 1864, 1868, 1874, from			
	£2	£12	£50
Four doubles, Heaton, 1885–1911, various dates from	£2	£7	£15
Four doubles, Heaton, broad shield, 1914–49, from	£2	£5	£10
Four doubles, Lily reverse, 1956			
	£1	£3	£6
Eight doubles, copper, 1834, 1858, from			
	£5	£26	£90
Eight doubles, bronze, (31mm), 1864			
	£3	£16	£50
Eight doubles, (32mm), 1868, 1874, from			
	£4	£10	£30
Eight doubles, Heaton, 1885–1911, various dates from	£3	£5	£20
Eight doubles, Heaton, straight-sided shield, 1914–49 from	£1	£2	£5
Eight doubles, Lilies reverse, 1956, 1959 from			
	50p	£1	£5

1956–59. Threepence.

Scalloped cupro-nickel. Obv: Shield in circle. Rev: Guernsey cow.

Threepence, thin flan, 1956			
	50p	£2	£3
Threepence, thick flan, 1959			
	25p	£1	£2

1966. Ninth Centenary of the Norman Conquest.

Diamond shaped with rounded corners. Cupronickel. Obv: Right-facing bust by Arnold Machin. Rev: Left-facing crowned effigy of William the Conqueror.

Ten shillings	£2	£3	£5

1968–71. First Decimal Coinage.

Alloys, weights and specifications as for the United Kingdom. Obv: Arms of Guernsey. Rev: Various pictorial motifs noted below. Values denominated in new pence.

	VF	Unc
Half new penny, numeral, 1971	10p	£1
New penny, gannet in flight, 1971	10p	£1
Two new pence, Sark Mill, 1971	10p	£1
Five new pence, Guernsey lily, 1968	10p	£1
Ten new pence, Guernsey cow, 1968, 1970	50p	£2
Fifty new pence, Cap of Duke of Normandy, 1969–70 from	£1	£3

1972. Royal Silver Wedding.

Obv: Arms on shield. Rev: Eros stepping on Guernsey lily. ELIZABETH AND PHILIP 1947 1972.

25p	£6

1977. Silver Jubilee.

Obv: Machin bust with dates 1952–1977. Rev: Castle Cornet.

25p	£2

1977–84. Second Decimal Coinage.

As above, but value expressed in pence.

Halfpenny (proof only), 1979	—	£2
Penny, 1977, 1979 from	10p	£1
Twopence, 1977, 1979 from	10p	£1
Five pence, 1977, 1979, 1982 from	15p	£1
Ten pence, 1977, 1979, 1982, 1984 from	30p	£2
Fifty pence, 1981–4, from	30p	£2
One pound, Guernsey lilies, 1981	£2	£3
One pound, HMS *Crescent*, 1983	£2	£3

1978. Royal Visit.

Obv: Machin bust. Rev: Heraldic shield flanked by date.

25p	£2

1980. Queen Mother's 80th Birthday.

Obv: Machin bust. Rev: Left-facing bust of the Queen Mother.

25p	£3

1981. Royal Wedding.

Obv: Machin bust. Rev: Prince Charles, Princess Diana, plumes and shield.

25p	£3

1982–97. Third Decimal Coinage.

Obv: Right-facing crowned profile by Raphael Maklouf with heraldic shield at the side. New reverse motifs noted below.

Penny, crab, 1985–90, 1992, 1994, 1997, from	10p	£1
Twopence, Guernsey cow, 1985–90, 1992, 1997, from	10p	£1
Five pence (24mm), sailing ship, 1985–90, from	10p	£1
Ten pence (28mm), Guernsey tomatoes, 1985–90, from	30p	£2
Twenty pence, milk can, 1982–3, from	40p	£2
Twenty pence, map in cogwheel, 1985–90, 1992, from	30p	£2
Fifty pence (30mm), Guernsey freesias, 1985–90, 1992, 1997 from	75p	£2
One pound, stylised £1, 1985–90, 1992, 1997, from	£2	£3
Two pounds, shield on cross, 1997	£4	£12

1985–95. Commemorative Crowns.

Cupro-nickel coins as previous 25p but revalued at £2 each. Also available as silver proofs (from £30) or piedforts of double weight (from £60).

40th Anniversary of Liberation, 1985	£10
Commonwealth Games, 1986	£10
900th Anniversary of the Death of William the Conqueror, 1987	£9
William II, 1988	£9
Henry I, 1989	£9
Royal Visit, 1989	£9
Queen Mother's 90th birthday, 1990	£9
Henry II, 1991	£9
40th Anniversary of the Coronation, 1993	£8
50th Anniversary of D-Day, 1994	£8
50th Anniversary of Liberation, 1995	£8

1990–97. Reduced Sizes.
Obv: Maklouf bust. Rev: Motifs as above. Coins reduced in size to conform to the UK specifications.

Five pence (18mm), 1990, 1992, 1997, from
10p £1
Ten pence (24.5mm), 1992, 1997, from
20p £1
Fifty pence (27.3mm), 1997 60p £1.50

1994. 50th Anniversary of the Normandy Landings.
Obv: Maklouf profile with heraldic shield at the side. Rev: Invasion scenes.
Issued as gold proofs only, £10, £25, £50 and £100 £900

1995. 50th Anniversary of Liberation.
Obv: Maklouf bust with heraldic shield at the side. Rev: Liberation scene.
Issued as gold proofs only, £10, £25, £50 and £100 £850

1995. Commemorative Crowns.
As 1985–95 but denominated £5. Prices are for cupro-nickel circulating coins. Silver proofs (from £40) were also struck.

Queen Mother's 95th Birthday, 1995	£15
Queen's 70th Birthday, 1996	£15
European Football Championships, 1996	£15
Royal Golden Wedding, 1997	£15
Castle Cornet, 1997	£12
Caernarfon Castle (silver proof only)	£40
Diana, the work continues, 2002	£12

1995. Gold Commemoratives.
Denominated £25.

Queen Mother's 95th Birthday, 1995	£220
Queen's 70th Birthday, 1996	£220
European Football Championships, 1996	£220
80th Anniversary of the Royal Air Force, 1998	£220
Royal Wedding, 1999	£220
Queen Mother, 1999	£200
Diana, the work continues, 2002	£200

1997. Fourth Decimal Coinage.
Obv: Profile by Ian Rank-Broadley.
Two pounds, shield on cross £3

1997. Silver Commemoratives.
Royal Golden Wedding, £10, 1997	£45
Millennium, £10, 1999	£50

150th Anniversary of the Death of Wellington, £5 £30

ALDERNEY

Since 1989 this island, which is a dependency of Guernsey, has issued numerous commemorative coins in cupro-nickel, silver proof, silver piedfort and gold. Unless otherwise stated we only list the cupro-nickel version.

Royal Visit £2, 1989	£7
Queen Mother's 90th Birthday £2, 1990	£8
40th Anniversary of the Accession £2, 1992	£8
40th Anniversary of the Coronation (silver proof) £1, 1993	£35
£25 gold proof only	£170
As above, £2, 1993	£8
50th Anniversary of the Normandy Landings £2, 1994	£8
£10 gold proof only	£75
£25 gold proof only	£200
£50 gold proof only	£250
£100 gold proof only	£475
50th Anniversary of Return of the Islanders £2, 1995	£8
Queen Mother's 95th Birthday, £5, 1995	£12
Queen's 70th Birthday, £5, 1996	£12
Worldwide Fund for Nature: Puffin, £2, 1997	£10
Royal Golden Wedding, £2, 1997	£8
£25 (gold proof only)	£210
Solar Eclipse, £5, 1999 (silver proof only)	£5
60th Anniversary of the Battle of Britain, £5, 2000	£10
£25 (gold proof only)	£200
150th Anniversary of the Death of Wellington, £5 (silver), 2002	£30
Prince William's 21st Birthday, 2003	£10

JERSEY

As in Guernsey, British and French currency circulated side by side in Jersey till the beginning of the 19th century when French money was banned. This coincided with the chronic shortage of coins in Britain and led to the issue of copper tokens by merchants on the island, as well as silver tokens by the States (parliament) of Jersey in 1813. A copper subsidiary coinage was introduced in 1841. Instead of doubles (as in Guernsey) Jersey opted for fractions of a shilling, creating some extremely awkward denominations which were not brought into line with the British mainland until 1877. The largest unit, equivalent to the mainland penny, was the thirteenth of a shilling, while the 26th and 52nd approximated to the halfpenny and farthing respectively.

1813. States of Jersey Tokens.
Obv: Arms in pointed shield. Rev: Date and value in words within a wreath.

	VF	EF	Unc
Eighteen pence	£75	£185	£420
Three shillings	£100	£300	£750

1841. Thirteenth Shilling Coinage.
Obv: Young head of Queen Victoria by William Wyon. Rev: Armorial shield.

	VF	EF	Unc
52nd shilling, copper, 1841	£20	£50	£120
26th shilling, copper, 1841, 1844, 1851, 1861, from	£8	£35	£125
26th shilling, bronze, 1870-71, from	£5	£15	£40
13th shilling, copper, 1841, 1844, 1851, 1858, 1861, from	£7	£32	£125
13th shilling, bronze, 1866, 1870–71, from	£5	£30	£70

1877. Twelfth Shilling Coinage.
Obv: Profile of Queen Victoria by Leonard Charles Wyon. Rev: Armorial shield.

	VF	EF	Unc
48th shilling, Heaton, 1877	£10	£45	£120
24th shilling, Heaton, 1877	£3	£7	£32
24th shilling, 1888, 1894	£3	£6	£30
12th shilling, Heaton, 1877	£2	£10	£35
12th shilling, 1881, 1888, 1894, from	£2	£8	£35

1909. Edward VII Coinage.
Obv: Right-facing crowned bust. Rev: Pointed shield.

	VF	EF	Unc
24th shilling, 1909	£3	£7	£30
12th shilling, 1909	£2	£10	£25

1911–35. George V Coinage.
Obv: Left-facing crowned bust. Rev: Pointed shield.

	VF	EF	Unc
24th shilling, 1911, 1913, 1923	£2	£5	£25
24th shilling, round shield with scrolls, 1923, 1926, from	£2	£4	£20
24th shilling, round shield, no scrolls, 1931, 1933, 1935	£1	£3	£10
12th shilling, 1911, 1913, 1923	£2	£5	£20
12th shilling, round shield with scrolls, 1923, 1926, from	£2	£4	£15
12th shilling, round shield, no scrolls, 1931, 1933, 1935	£2	£4	£10

1937–47. George VI Coinage.
Obv: Left-facing crowned profile. Rev: Armorial shield.

	VF	EF	Unc
24th shilling, 1937, 1946, 1947	£1	£3	£10
12th shilling, 1937, 1946, 1947	£2	£4	£8
12th shilling, LIBERATED 1945 (1949–52)			£2
	5p	50p	£3

1954–66. Elizabeth II Coinage.
Obv: Right-facing crowned bust. Rev: Armorial shield. Commemorative inscriptions below shields on coins of 1960 and 1966.

	VF	EF	Unc
12th shilling, LIBERATED 1945 (1954)	25p	50p	£3
12th shilling, 1957	30p	50p	£3
12th shilling, Restoration tercentenary, 1960	20p	40p	£3
12th shilling, Norman Conquest, 1966	10p	50p	£2
4th shilling, circular, 1957	£1	£2	£5
4th shilling, 12-sided flan, 1964	50p	£1	£3
4th shilling, Norman Conquest, 1966	50p	£1	£3
Five shillings, Norman Conquest, 1966	£2	£4	£6

1968–80. First Decimal Coinage.
Obv: Right-facing bust by Arnold Machin. Rev: Armorial shield, unless otherwise stated. Coins denominated in new pence.

	EF	Unc
Half new penny, 1971, 1980	10p	£1
New penny, 1971, 1980	10p	£1
Two new pence, 1971, 1975, 1980	10p	£1
Five new pence, 1968, 1980	15p	£1
Ten new pence, 1968, 1975, 1980	20p	£1
Fifty new pence, 1969, 1980	75p	£2

1972. Royal Silver Wedding.
Obv: Machin bust. Rev: Various motifs noted below.

	EF	Unc
Fifty pence, mace on island map	£1.50	£3
One pound, Jersey lilies	£1.50	£3

Two pounds, schooner *Alexandra*
          £2.50   £4
Two and a half pounds, lobster   £5   £8
Five pounds (gold), lesser white-toothed shrew
             —   £35
Ten pounds (gold), gold torque, 1500 BC
             —   £50
Twenty pounds (gold), ormer shell   —   £80
Twenty five pounds (gold), arms of Elizabeth I
             —   £120
Fifty pounds (gold), heraldic shield   —   £200

1977. Silver Jubilee.
Obv: Machin bust. Rev: Mont Orgeuil Castle and Gorey Harbour.
Twenty five pence   £1   £2

1981. Bicentenary of the Battle of Jersey.
Obv: Machin bust. Rev: Crowned arms over a cross. Rounded diamond shape.
One pound   £1.30   £2

1981. Second Decimal Coinage.
As 1968–80 but denominations in pence.
Half penny   10p   £1
Penny   10p   £1
Two pence   10p   £1
Five pence   15p   £1
Ten pence   20p   £1.50
Fifty pence   75p   £3

1982. Third Decimal Coinage.
Obv: Machin bust. Rev: Pictorial motifs noted below. As in the UK, the reverse of the pound coins has been changed semi-annually since 1983, featuring arms of the parishes (1983-89) and then sailing ships (1991-94). Prices in uncirculated condition are for those in the specimen folders.
Penny. Le Hocq Tower, 1983   10p   £1
Two pence, L'Hermitage, 1983   10p   £1
Five pence (24mm), Seymour Tower 1983-88
             10p   £1
Five pence (18mm), 1990-   10p   £1
Ten pence (28.5mm), La Hougue Bie, 1983-90
             15p   £1
Ten pence (4.5mm), 1992   15p   £1
Twenty pence, Corbiere Lighthouse, dated reverse, 1982   50p   £1
Twenty pence, dated obverse, 1983 25p   £1
Fifty pence (30mm), Grosnez Castle, 1983–97
             75p   £2
Fifty pence (27mm), 1997   75p   £2
Pound, St Helier, 1983   £1.50   £5

Pound, St Saviour, 1984   £1.50   £7
Pound, St Brelade, 1984   £1.50   £7
Pound, St Clement, 1985   £1.50   £7
Pound, St Lawrence, 1985   £1.50   £8
Pound, St Peter, 1986   £1.50   £8
Pound, Grouville. 1986   £1.50   £8
Pound, St Martin, 1987   £1.50   £8
Pound, St Ouen, 1987   £1.50   £5
Pound, Trinity, 1988   £1.50   £6
Pound, St John, 1988   £1.50   £7
Pound, St Mary, 1989   £1.50   £7
Pound, *Tickler*, 1991   £1.50   £6
Pound, *Percy Douglas*, 1991   £1.50   £5
Pound, *Hebe*, 1992   £1.50   £5
Pound, *Coat of Arms*, 1992   £1.50   £5
Pound, *Gemini*, 1993   £1.50   £5
Pound, *Century*, 1993   £1.50   £5
Pound, Rank-Broadley bust / *Resolute*, 1994
             £1.50   £5

1997. Bi-metallic Coinage.
Obv: Machin bust. Rev: £2 within a circle of parish shields. Cupro-nickel centre and brass outer ring.
Two pounds, 1997   £2.50   £3
Two pounds, Rank-Broadley bust, 1998
             £2.50   £3

Commemorative Coins since 1981.
Since 1981 Jersey has issued a large number of commemorative coins, the vast majority in proof silver or gold versions. Space prevents a detailed listing and they are briefly summarised here. Prices are quoted for the cupro-nickel coins unless otherwise stated.
Royal Wedding, Charles and Diana, £2, 1981
             £10
40th Anniversary of Liberation, £2, 1985   £5
Commonwealth Games, £2, 1986   £8
World Wildlife Fund, 25th anniversary, £2, 1987   £8
Royal Visit, £2, 1989   £8
Queen Mother's 90th Birthday, £2, 1990   £7
50th Anniversary of the Battle of Britain £2, 1990 (silver)   £40
£5 (5 ounce silver)   £95
£10 (gold)   £170
£25 (gold)   £220
£50 (gold)   £300
£100 (gold)   £400
40th Anniversary of the Coronation £2, 1993
             £8
50th Anniversary of Liberation, £2, 1995   £10
£10 (gold)   £170

£25 (gold)	£220
£50 (gold)	£300
£100 (gold)	£400
Queen's 70th Birthday, £2, 1996	£8

ISLE OF MAN

Lying in the Irish Sea midway between Scotland, Ireland and Lancashire, the Isle of Man was formerly part of the great Viking empire. After the Battle of Largs in 1263 it passed under Scottish rule but Edward I seized it in 1290 and from 1333 onwards it came under the feudal overlordship of the English rulers, who permitted the native rulers to continue. William Montacute, Earl of Salisbury, was crowned King of Man in 1334, but later it was governed by the Stanley family, Earls of Derby who were Lords of Man from 1406 till 1736 when the Derby heiress married the second Duke of Atholl. In 1765 the third Duke gave up his sovereignty to the Crown and since then the British monarch has been Lord of Man. The island retained its political identity and Tynwald (founded in 979) is regarded as the world's oldest parliament in continuous existence. Viking pennies and Irish tokens circulated on the island over the centuries but distinctive coinage may be said to date from 1679 when John Murrey produced brass tokens. The tenth Earl of Derby issued copper coins in 1709 and his successor produced coins in 1733–34. The second Duke of Atholl issued halfpence and pennies in 1758. After the Revestment Act of 1765 British coins took over, distinctive coins with the triskeles reverse being produced in 1786 and 1813. Copper coins were struck in 1839 but were withdrawn as a result of the Copper Riots of 1840 which arose when the government retariffed the penny at 12 instead of 14 to the shilling. The islanders believed that they were being robbed of twopence in the shilling and the unrest was only quelled by withdrawing the Manx coinage. Gold coins were issued in 1965 to celebrate the bicentenary of the Revestment Act, followed by a Manx cat crown in 1970. The following year, the Isle of Man introduced decimal coinage with the same weights and specifications as the United Kingdom. The initial series was struck by the Royal Mint but since 1972 all coins have been produced by the Pobjoy Mint. The Isle of Man has the unenviable reputation of producing

more coins per capita than anywhere else in the world. Consequently only a brief outline of the coins since 1972 are possible within the scope of this catalogue.

1709. First Derby Coinage.

Obv: Derby arms (eagle and child on a cap of maintenance) with French motto SANS CHANGER (without change) and date. Rev: Triskeles and Latin motto QVOCVNQVE GESSERIS STABIT (whichever way you throw it, it will stand).

	F	VF	EF
Halfpenny, various types from			
	£30	£50	£150
Penny, various types from £25	£65	£160

733. Second Derby Coinage

...imilar to first issue but better execution and ...bverse and reverse contained in beaded ...ircles.

...alfpenny, various types and alloys from
| | £20 | £40 | £150 |

...enny, various types and alloys from
| | £12 | £25 | £120 |

758. Atholl Coinage.

...bv: Ducal coronet over AD and date. Rev: ...riskeles and motto correctly spelled QUO-...UNQUE JECERIS STABIT.

| ...alfpenny | £20 | £35 | £135 |
| ...enny | £15 | £30 | £125 |

1786. George III First Coinage.

Obv: Right-facing laureated bust. Rev: Triskeles and motto. Engraved by Lewis Pingo and struck at the Royal Mint.

Halfpenny, various types from
| | £15 | £30 | £70 |
| Penny, various types from £15 | £40 | £125 |

1798–1813. George III Second Coinage.

Obv: Right-facing laureated bust. Rev: Triskeles and motto. Incuse inscriptions on raised rims. Engraved by Conrad Heinrich Küchler and struck at the Soho Mint, Birmingham.

Halfpenny, GEORGIUS, 1798
| | £15 | £25 | £65 |

Halfpenny, annulets, GEORGIVS, 1813
| | £15 | £30 | £70 |

Penny, no annulets below truncation, 1798
| | £15 | £45 | £120 |
Penny, annulets, 1813
| | £12 | £35 | £100 |

1839. Victorian Coinage.

Obv: Left-facing Young Head profile. Rev: Triskeles and motto. Engraved by William Wyon and struck at the Royal Mint.

Farthing	£15	£25	£50
Halfpenny	£15	£30	£45
Penny	£10	£25	£75

1965. Bicentenary of the Revestment Act

Obv: Machin bust. Rev: Triskeles in a shield surrounded by Hiberno-Norse ring-chain. Struck i .917 gold at the Royal Mint.

	EF	Unc
Half sovereign		£5
Sovereign		£7
Five pounds		£40

1970. Manx Cat.

Obv: Machin bust. Rev: Manx cat by Christopher Ironside. Struck by the Royal Canadian Mint, Ottawa.

Crown   £1   £3

1971. First Decimal Coinage.

Obv: Machin bust inscribed ELIZABETH THE SECOND. Rev: various motifs noted below. Struck at the Royal Mint (no mint-marks).

Half new penny, St John's wort, 1971
                        10p   £1
New penny, Hiberno-Norse ring-chain, 1971
                        10p   £1
Two new pence, pair of peregrine falcons, 1971
                        10p   £1
Five new pence, Tower of Refuge, Douglas, 1971   10p   £1
Ten new pence, Triskeles, 1971   20p   £1
Fifty new pence, Viking longship, 1971
                        75p   £2

1972. Royal Silver Wedding.

Obv: Machin bust. Rev: Conjoined shields of the Queen and Duke of Edinburgh. Struck by the Royal Canadian Mint, Ottawa.

Crown   £1   £3

Coins since 1972.

The contract to design, manufacture, market and distribute Isle of Man coins passed in 1972 to the Pobjoy Mint of Sutton, Surrey. Over the past 30 years, the number of coins has escalated dramatically. Not only are coins produced in various versions (circulating, specimen, diamond finish or proof) but also in silver, gold and platinum and even, in recent years, with precious stones inset. There have been coins with holograms and coins with coloured surfaces, coins with different metals inset and even coins in three different contrasting alloys. Coins of the same date have been released with a wide variety of privy marks of a quasi-commemorative nature, die marks and different edge marks. Apart from these gimmicks, the range of coin designs has been overwhelming, now running to several hundreds. There have been silver, gold and platinum bullion issues, Christmas and Chinese New Year coins, Tourist Trophy race coins and an enormous number of issues for every conceivable event from the Olympic Games and World Cup football championships to purely thematic series featuring breeds of cats and dogs, flower fairies and even Harry Potter. These confections, although nominally classed as legal tender, are widely regarded as pseudo coins and are therefore outside the scope of this catalogue. Below, we list only those coins which we consider had a legitimate circulation as actual currency.

1972–75. Second Decimal Coinage.

Obverse and reverse as Royal mint series but PM mint-mark below the Queen's bust. Struck by the Pobjoy Mint. Only 1000 of each coin dated 1972-74 was struck retrospectively and put into general circulation. Prices are for the 1975 coins.

Half new penny, 1972–75, from	10p	£1
New penny, 1972–75, from	10p	£1
Two new pence, 1972–75, from	10p	£1
Ten new pence, 1972–75, from	15p	£1
Fifty new pence, 1972–75, from	60p	£2

1976–79. Third Decimal Coinage.

Obv: Machin bust inscribed ISLE OF MAN ELIZABETH II. Rev: New motifs superimposed on a map of the island noted below. Values denominated in pence.

Halfpenny, herring, 1976, 1978–79	10p	£1
Halfpenny, FOOD FOR ALL below map, 1977		
	20p	£1.50
Penny, Loaghtyn ram, 1976–79	10p	£1
Two pence, Manx shearwater, 1976–79		
	10p	£1
Five pence, Laxey wheel, 1976–79	10p	£1
Ten pence, Triskeles, 1976–79	15p	£1
Fifty pence, Viking longship, 1976–79		
	£75	£2
Pound, Triskeles, 1978–81	£1.20	£2

1979–80. Millennium of Tynwald.
Obv: Machin bust. Rev: Viking replica ship Odin's Raven off Point of Ayre. Millennium logo on sail. Edge incuse inscription H.M.Q.E.II ROYAL VISIT I.O.M.

Fifty pence, 1979	£1	£3
Fifty pence, 1980, edge VIKING EXHIBN NEW YORK		
	£1	£3

1980–84. Fourth Decimal Coinage.
Obv: Machin bust. Rev: Pictorial motifs with Hiberno-Norse ornament.

Halfpenny, 1980–83, herring	10p	£1
Halfpenny, FAO coin as 1977 but dated 1981		
	10p	£1.50
Halfpenny, 1981, inscribed WORLD FOOD DAY		
	10p	£1
Penny, Manx cat, 1981–83	10p	£1
Two pence, chough, 1980–83	10p	£1
Five pence, Loaghtyn ram, 1980–83		
	15p	£1

Ten pence, peregrine falcon, 1980–83		
	20p	£1
Twenty pence, trophy of arms, 1982–83		
	35p	£1.50
Fifty pence, Gokstad ship, 1980–83		
	75p	£2
One pound, arms of Peel, 1983	£1.20	£2
One pound, arms of Castletown, 1984		
	£1.20	£2
One pound, arms of Ramsey, 1985		
	£1.20	£2
Five pounds, triskeles on map, 1981–84		
	£6	£7.50

1984. Fifth Decimal Coinage.
Obv: Machin bust. Rev: Various motifs set in a quasi-heraldic shield to celebrate the Quincentenary of the College of Heralds.

Halfpenny, fuchsia	10p	£1
Penny, shag on a tilting shield	10p	£1
Two pence, peregrine falcon	15p	£1
Five pence, cushag flower	15p	£1
Ten pence, Loaghtyn rampant	20p	£1
Twenty pence, three herrings couchant		
	35p	£1.50
Fifty pence, lymphad galley	75p	£2
Five pounds, knight on horseback	£6	£10

1985–87. Sixth Decimal Coinage.
Obv: Maklouf bust. Rev: as heraldic series of 1984.

Halfpenny, fuchsia, 1985	10p	£1
Penny, shag, 1985–87	10p	£1
Two pence, peregrine falcon, 1985–87		
	10p	£1
Five pence, cushag flower, 1985–87		
	10p	£1
Ten pence, Loaghtyn, 1985–87	15p	£1
Twenty pence, three herrings, 1985–87		
	25p	£1
Fifty pence, lymphad, 1985–87	75p	£2
One pound, arms of Ramsey, 1985		
	£1.20	£2
One pound, arms of Douglas, 1986		
	£1.20	£2
Two pounds, Tower of Refuge, 1986–87		
	£2.50	£3
Five pounds, knight on horseback, 1985–87		
	£6	£9

1988–95. Seventh Decimal Coinage.
Obv: Maklouf bust. Rev: Various motifs illustrating modern Manx trade and industry, with name Ellan Vannin in Manx Gaelic.

Penny, precision tools, 1988–95	10p	30p

Penny, Rugby ball and goalposts, 1996	10p	50p
Two pence, stone cross and tools, 1988–95	10p	30p
Two pence, cyclists, 1996	10p	30p
Five pence (24mm), windsurfing, 1988–90	20p	50p
Five pence (18mm), windsurfing, 1990–93	20p	50p
Five pence, golf clubs and ball, 1994–95	20p	50p
Five pence, golfer, 1996	10p	30p
Ten pence (28.5mm), map and portcullis, 1988–92	20p	50p
Ten pence (24.5mm), triskeles, 1992–95	20p	50p
Ten pence, sail boat, 1996	20p	50p
Twenty pence, combine harvester, 1988–93	40p	£1
Twenty pence, raised border, 1993–95	40p	£1
Twenty pence, rally cars, 1996	50p	£1
Fifty pence (30mm), computer, 1988–95	75p	£2
Fifty pence (30mm), TT riders, 1996–97	£1	£3
One pound, warrior on horseback, 1987	£1.20	£2
One pound, telecommunications, 1988–95	£1.20	£2
One pound, cricket equipment, 1996	£1.20	£2
One pound, arms of Douglas, 1996	£1.20	£2
Two pounds, Manx airlines, 1988–92	£2.50	£3
Two pounds, airship, 1989	—	—
Two pounds, Nigel Mansell racing driver, 1993	£2.50	£3
Two pounds, racing cars, 1994	£2.50	£3
Two pounds, British Legion emblem, 1995	£2.50	£3
Two pounds, rally cars, 1996	£2.50	£3
Two pounds, as 1996 but bi-metallic, 1997	£2.50	£3
Five pounds, lobster boat, 1988–92	£6	£9
Five pounds, Nigel Mansell, 1993	£6	£10
Five pounds, racing cars, 1994	£6	£10
Five pounds, Winston Churchill, 1995	£6	£10
Five pounds, European Football Championship, 1996	£6	£10
Five pounds, Royal Golden Wedding, 1997	£6	£10

1998. Eighth Decimal Coinage.

Obv: Profile by Ian Rank-Broadley. Rev: Sport motifs, as 1996.

Penny, Rugby ball and goalposts	10p	30
Two pence, cyclists	10p	30
Five pence, golfer	10p	30
Ten pence, sail boat	15p	30
Twenty pence, rally cars	25p	50
Fifty pence, TT riders	75p	£
One pound, cricket equipment	£1.20	£
Two pounds, racing cars	£2.50	£
Five pounds, footballers	£6	£9

Where can I learn how to clean my coin collection at 2:00 in the morning?

www.collectorcafe.com
(You don't have to wait until 2am - Go there now!)

- contact fellow collectors from all over the world

- free classified advertising

- links to hundreds of other interesting collecting sites

- 90 collecting categories, including **coins**

- your chance to contribute an article or two on any collecting interest of your choice

Collector Cafe is the **free** collectibles site sponsored by Stanley Gibbons. It is a forum for everybody to share news and views about collecting with fellow enthusiasts from every corner of the globe.

For more information, please contact us at

info@collectorcafe.com

Collector C@fe

The world's largest online collecting community
w w w . c o l l e c t o r c a f e . c o m

The market in British coins is strong, with the average very fine condition coin increasing by 15% in 2003 backed by a solid collector base. As you can see from the examples highlighted below, there have been a number of coins recording phenomenal increases in value.

Charles 1	1997	2004	% Growth
1642 Triple Unite	£5250	£8500	61.90%

Condition is paramount with coins and we are proud to be able to offer only the best quality, investment grade items. Coins are portable tangible assets that are small, easy to store and have a worldwide market. Rare gold coins also have an underlying intrinsic value and are never worth less than their weight in gold.

George III	1997	2004	% Growth
1813 Military Guinea	£800	£1750	118.75%

Mary	1997	2004	% Growth
Fine Sovereign	£4500	£7250	61.11%

The Stanley Gibbons Investment Department is forging a reputation for expert guidance and supplying portfolios that record excellent growth in value. If you would like to find out more about our alternative investment options please do not hesitate to contact a member of our Investment Department on **+ 44 (0)20 7557 4454**. Please contact us for an informal discussion, investment advice or simply to learn more about the services we offer. We also have **sample portfolios** available to highlight the quality that we can supply.

www.stanleygibbons.com/investment